Houghton Mifflin Science

DiscoveryWorks

TEACHING GUIDE / 4

Magnetism and Electricity

Welcome

to Houghton Mifflin **Science DiscoveryWorks** — a science program that provides a balance of exciting hands-on activities and engaging content resources. **Science DiscoveryWorks** reflects our belief that effective science education gradually introduces students to the knowledge, methods, skills, and attitudes of scientists, while simultaneously recognizing and respecting the educational and developmental needs of all students.

HOUGHTON MIFFLIN

Boston • Atlanta • Dallas • Denver • Geneva, Illinois • Palo Alto • Princeton

Acknowledgments appear on pages A82, B70, C72, D82, E104, which constitute extensions of this copyright page.

Printed in the U.S.A.

Grade 4 One-Volume Teaching Guide   ISBN 0-618-00865-9   2 3 4 5 6 7 8 9-WEB-05 04 03 02 01 00

Grade 4 Modular Teaching Guides

Unit A: Earth's Land   ISBN 0-618-00297-9   3 4 5 6 7 8 9-WEB-05 04 03 02 01 00

Unit B: Properties of Matter   ISBN 0-618-00298-7   3 4 5 6 7 8 9-WEB-05 04 03 02 01 00

Unit C: Classifying Living Things   ISBN 0-618-00299-5   3 4 5 6 7 8 9-WEB-05 04 03 02 01 00

Unit D: Magnetism and Electricity   ISBN 0-618-00300-2   3 4 5 6 7 8 9-WEB-05 04 03 02 01 00

Unit E: Weather and Climate   ISBN 0-618-00301-0   3 4 5 6 7 8 9-WEB-05 04 03 02 01 00

ABOUT THE PROGRAM

THE AUTHORS

Coming From Diverse Backgrounds, Meeting on Common Ground

William Badders

Elementary Science Teacher,
Cleveland Public Schools, Cleveland, OH

A 1992 Presidential Award winner, Mr. Badders teaches science to students in Grades K through 6. He was a member of the Working Group on Science Assessment Standards. He is a member of the Board of Directors of the National Science Teachers Association. He specializes in the biological and physical sciences.

Dr. Lowell J. Bethel

Professor of Science Education,
The University of Texas at Austin, Austin, TX

Dr. Bethel recently served as Program Director for Teacher Enhancement at the National Science Foundation. He specializes in the biological and physical sciences, urban and multicultural education, constructivism, and the development and evaluation of in-service science programs.

Dr. Victoria Fu

Professor of Child Development and Early Childhood Education, Virginia Polytechnic Institute and State University, Blacksburg, VA

Dr. Fu has extensive experience in teaching child development and teacher education. She has been involved, nationally and internationally, in teacher education initiatives based on qualitative inquiry. Her current research and writings focus on young children as learners and inquirers.

Donald Peck

Director (retired), The Center for Elementary Science,
Fairleigh Dickinson University, Madison, NJ

Mr. Peck's extensive experience in science education includes conducting more than 500 hands-on science workshops for elementary school teachers. He also was a K–12 science supervisor for 23 years. He specializes in the physical and earth sciences.

Dr. Carolyn Sumners

Director of Astronomy and Physical Sciences,
Houston Museum of Natural Science, Houston, TX

Dr. Sumners directs the museum's Burke Baker Planetarium, Challenger Learning Center, and technology camps. She also curates the museum's Welch Chemistry Hall, Fondren Discovery Place, and Arnold Hall of Space Sciences. She is project director for the Toys in Space program at the Johnson Space Center and is a published author of children's books.

Catherine Valentino

Author-in-Residence – Houghton Mifflin,
West Kingston, RI

Ms. Valentino has extensive experience as a classroom teacher, a curriculum coordinator, and a director of elementary education. In her current position, she specializes in developing educational materials that integrate inquiry-based learning and problem-solving skills in all of the content areas. At the University of Rhode Island she serves as Curriculum Advisor for SMILE (Science and Math Investigative Learning Experiences), an after-school enrichment program for students in Grades 4–12.

Reading Consultant
Dr. Peter Dewitz

Educational Consultant
Charlottesville, VA

Dr. Peter Dewitz is a reading expert who specializes in the comprehension of informational text. He was an elementary school teacher in Los Angeles before moving to college teaching and research at the University of Toledo and most recently at the University of Virginia. Currently Dr. Dewitz is working with various school districts to restructure reading instruction.

Sheltered English Consultant
Ronald Rohac

Faculty Member,
California State University-Long Beach, Long Beach, CA

Ron Rohac has been a classroom teacher for 22 years, with extensive background and experience in working with Limited English Proficient students. Mr. Rohac is currently a faculty member at California State University, Long Beach, and is a well-known consultant who creates staff development programs, classroom strategies, and program design for state departments and school districts all over the United States.

We believe . . .

As individuals we come from a variety of backgrounds, but as educators we meet on common ground. We share a vision of effective science education for all children. Our vision is based on these principles.

Our Principles

- Students learn science concepts most effectively through a balance of hands-on activities and solid content knowledge. We provide students with many opportunities to use science process skills and the methods of science through hands-on activities. In addition, we provide solid content resources to help students understand their hands-on exploration.

- In a world that is growing increasingly dependent on the contributions of science, scientific literacy is an important educational goal for all students. In this program we teach students to use science process skills, critical-thinking skills, and scientific reasoning skills to help develop scientific literacy.

- Assessment is an ongoing process that should be used to guide instruction. The variety of assessment in *DiscoveryWorks* enables teachers to tailor assessment to student needs and abilities.

- Science education is enhanced when based upon reliable educational standards that guide student attainment, curriculum content, and teaching practices. *Science DiscoveryWorks* is based on the Benchmarks for Science Literacy prepared by Project 2061, a long-term educational reform project of the American Association for the Advancement of Science, and the National Science Education Standards prepared by the National Research Council.

The Authors

CONSULTANTS & REVIEWERS

Jean Blackshear
Fred A. Toomer Elementary Sch.
Atlanta, GA

Frank A. Bodgen, Jr.
Carver Elementary
Henderson, NC

Bonnie Bohrer
Brookview Elementary School
Brook Park, OH

Robert L. Burtch
1990 Presidential Award winner
Batavia Middle School
Batavia, IL

Martha Christine
Calypso Elementary School
Bethlehem, PA

Mary Eve Corrigan
The Columbus Academy
Gahanna, OH

Patty Dadonna
Hollywood Elementary
Hollywood, FL

John S. Detrick
Emeritus Dept. Chair of
Mathematics, holder of the
McElroy Chair of Mathematics
The Columbus Academy
Gahanna, OH

Robert C. Dixon
National Center to Improve the
Tools of Educators (NCITE)
University of Oregon, College of
Education
Eugene, OR

Denise Pitts-Downing
James Elverson Middle School
Philadelphia, PA

Michaeline A. Dudas
Science and Math Instructional
Support/Consultant
Northbrook, IL

William Dudrow
The Columbus Academy
Gahanna, OH

Terri Dyer
Lake Weston Elementary
Orlando, FL

Barbara Elliott
1990 Presidential Award winner
Ray E. Kilmer Elementary School
Colorado Springs, CO

Fred Fabry
Retired teacher of Geology and
Biology
Deerfield High School
Deerfield, IL

Debbie Fitzpatrick
School 14
Clifton, NJ

Rhea Foster
Anderson Park Elementary Sch.
Atlanta, GA

Audrey Ann Fredrick
James Bowie Elementary
San Antonio, TX

Linda Froschauer
1993 Presidential Award winner
Weston Middle School
Weston, CT

Joanne Gallagher
Tamarac Middle School
Melrose, NY

Donna Green
Beauclerc Elementary
Jacksonville, FL

Marlene Gregor
Elem. Science Consultant
Bloomington, IL

Kim Grimme
Ponderosa Elementary
Sunnyvale, CA

Becca Stein Gutwirth
Florence M. Gaudineer School
Springfield, NJ

William L. Handy, Jr.
Parkland School District
Orefield, PA

Beverly Hanrahan
Franconia Elementary School
Souderton, PA

Renee Harris
Northwestern Lehigh Mid. Sch.
New Tripoli, PA

Patricia Heavens
Dunbar Elementary
East St. Louis, IL

Rhonda Hicks
James Elverson Middle School
Philadelphia, PA

Sr. Marie Patrice
Hoare, S.L.
Loretto Middle School
El Paso, TX

Nancy Hronkin
Forest Park Elementary
Crystal Falls, MI

Gail Hurst
Dr. Philips Elementary
Orlando, FL

Lester Y. Ichinose, Ph.D.
Evanston, IL

Mace A. Ishida, Ph.D.
Diversity and Ed. Consultant
Blacklick, OH

Kristine D. Jackson
Belleville, IL

Pearline A. James
W. F. Slaton Elementary School
Atlanta, GA

Evette Jones
Grover Cleveland Elementary
Philadelphia, PA

Charlene Kalinski
Gilvert Cuellar Elementary
Dallas, TX

Sr. Sharon Kassing, S.L.
St. Pius Catholic School
Kirkwood, MO

Jill Kersh
Bullock Elementary
Garland, TX

Gail Kirkland
Hiawassee Elementary
Orlando, FL

John Kibler
InterAmerica Intercultural
Training Institute
Des Plaines, IL

Jennifer Kimble
Rogers Elementary
Dallas, TX

Diane Landschoot
John N. C. Stockton Elementary
Jacksonville, FL

Bonnie Lawhorn
Evening Street Elementary
Worthington, OH

Sharon Lempner
R. G. Jones School
Cleveland, OH

Barbara Leonard
1992 Presidential Award winner
Heritage Elementary School
Pueblo, CO

Gus Liss
Young Elementary School
Burlington, NJ

Jo Ann Liss
Intervale School
Parsippany, NJ

Marlenn Maicki
1990 Presidential Award winner
Detroit Country Day School
Bloomfield Hills, MI

Lynn Malok
Spring Garden Elementary Sch.
Bethlehem, PA

Barbara Mecker
Rockwood South Middle Sch.
St. Louis, MO

Leonardo Melton
Fred A. Toomer Elementary Sch.
Atlanta, GA

Bonniejean Meyer
Tremont Elementary School
Cleveland, OH

Laura Mobbett
Huff School
Mountain View, CA

Dr. Suzanne Moore
L. L. Hotchkiss Elementary Sch.
Dallas, TX

Kathy Morton
Christ the King School
Atlanta, GA

Debora Multisano
Clair-Mel Elementary
Tampa, FL

Dr. Ngoc-Diep T. Nguyen
Director, Bilingual and
Multicultural Program
Schaumburg, IL

Michael O'Shea
R. G. Jones School
Cleveland, OH

Wendy Peterson
Harvey Rice Elementary School
Cleveland, OH

Filomena Poli-Aleman
Clifton Public School #4
Clifton, NJ

Alexandra Pond
Science Coordinator
North Shore School
Chicago, IL

Herb Quon
Spangler Elementary
Milipitas, CA

Terry Ramirez
Lackland City Elementary
San Antonio, TX

José Salas
Hooper Ave. School
Los Angeles, CA

Erika Silverman
Public School 41
Bronx, NY

Debi Sitkoski
Forest Park Elementary
Crystal Falls, MI

Chris Spigarelli
Forest Park Elementary
Crystal Falls, MI

Christine Spinner
Parkview Elementary
Parma, OH

Jean Ann Strillacci
Kennedy Elementary School
Succasunna, NJ

Laura Swanson
WATTS Intermediate School
Burlington City, NJ

Arthur F. Tobia
Public School 41
Bronx, NY

Laura Turner
Clover Flat Elementary
Boulevard, CA

Nancy Vibeto
1993 Presidential Award winner
Jim Hill Middle School
Minot, ND

Kathy Westbrook
Bluffsview Elementary
Columbus, OH

Sandra Wilson
McKinley Elementary School
Abington, PA

Bonita Wylie
Minnewashta Elementary
Excelsior, MN

THE SCOPE OF THE PROGRAM
An Overview of Concepts and Themes

	KINDERGARTEN	GRADE 1	GRADE 2
Life Science 	**UNIT A Characteristics of Living Things** Classification of objects as living or nonliving; basic needs and stages of growth of living things **Themes:** *Systems, Constancy and Change*	**UNIT A Kinds of Living Things** The similarities and differences between plants and animals; classifying plants and animals according to one characteristic; life cycles of plants and animals **Theme:** *Systems*	**UNIT A Interactions of Living Things** The needs of living things; plant and animal adaptations to various habitats; the effect of living things and natural forces on environments **Themes:** *Constancy and Change, Models*
	UNIT E Body Parts Identification of internal and external body parts; the functions and importance of individual body parts, including the hands, bones, muscles, heart, stomach, and brain **Themes:** *Systems, Models*	**UNIT E Keeping Fit and Healthy** The importance of good nutrition, exercise, sleep, and proper hygiene; the food pyramid and a healthful diet **Themes:** *Systems, Constancy and Change*	**UNIT E What Makes Me Sick** How germs cause illness; how illnesses spread; prevention of illnesses and injuries; how to stay healthy **Themes:** *Systems, Scale*
Physical Science 	**UNIT B Exploring With the Senses** Using the senses to observe the physical characteristics of objects; grouping objects by their physical characteristics **Theme:** *Systems*	**UNIT C Magnets** The properties of magnets; magnetic force; magnetic fields; temporary magnets; magnets and compasses **Themes:** *Systems, Scale*	**UNIT B Energy and Motion** Characteristics of light; measuring motion; how forces affect motion; sound waves, pitch, and volume; heat energy and uses of natural resources for heat **Themes:** *Constancy and Change, Scale*
	UNIT D Pushes and Pulls Different ways things move; pushes and pulls; surfaces; directional motion **Themes:** *Systems, Models*		**UNIT D Solids, Liquids, and Gases** Properties of solids, liquids, and gases; the changing of materials from one state to another **Theme:** *Constancy and Change*
Earth Science 	**UNIT C Looking at the Earth and Sky** Landforms; daytime sky and the sun; changing seasons and the weather; the moon and the stars **Themes:** *Constancy and Change, Scale*	**UNIT B Weather and Seasons** Factors that affect the weather; seasonal weather changes; how people, plants, and animals respond to weather conditions **Theme:** *Constancy and Change*	**UNIT C Changes Over Time** Characteristics of different dinosaurs; how trace fossils and fossil remains provide clues about the earth's history; changes in the day and night sky; daily and seasonal weather patterns **Themes:** *Models, Scale, Constancy and Change*
	 	**UNIT D Earth's Land and Water** Properties of soil and rocks; how water and soil mix; how water flows; recycling soil, water, and rocks **Themes:** *Systems, Models*	

> *The science that all students are expected to learn is defined so that students have sufficient time to develop a deep understanding of essential scientific ideas rather than superficial acquaintance with many isolated facts.*
>
> National Science Education Standards

GRADE 3	GRADE 4	GRADE 5	GRADE 6
UNIT A Life Cycles Stages in the life cycles of animals and plants; changes in animals and plants as they mature; inherited traits; ways that animals and plants survive **Theme:** *Models*	**UNIT C Classifying Living Things** Classification of living things; characteristics of different animal and plant groups; basic needs of living things; adaptations that help living things meet their needs. **Theme:** *Systems*	**UNIT A Systems in Living Things** Life processes of plants and animals; structure of plant and animal cells; human digestive, respiratory, circulatory, and excretory systems; life cycles of plants and animals **Theme:** *Systems*	**UNIT A Cells and Microbes** Structure and life processes of cells, including mitosis; protists and fungi; bacteria and viruses **Theme:** *Models*
UNIT E Roles of Living Things The needs of living things in relation to their environments; how living things adapt to their environments, change them, and respond to them **Theme:** *Constancy and Change*		**UNIT D Populations and Ecosystems** Dynamic interactions of living and nonliving things in an ecosystem; how energy and matter flow through an ecosystem; biomes; biodiversity **Theme:** *Systems*	**UNIT D Continuity of Life** Asexual reproduction; sexual reproduction, including meiosis; inherited and acquired traits; evolution, including evidence for evolution and evolutionary processes **Theme:** *Constancy and Change*
UNIT C Matter, Energy, and Forces Properties, states, and changes in matter; forms of energy and how heat energy moves and changes matter; forces and machines **Theme:** *Systems*	**UNIT B Properties of Matter** Physical properties; states; effects of heat loss or gain and of physical and chemical changes **Theme:** *Scale*	**UNIT C Matter and Energy** Properties of matter; states of matter; elements, compounds, and mixtures; forms of energy; energy transfer; changes In energy; changes in matter **Theme:** *Models*	**UNIT C The Nature of Matter** Physical and chemical properties; elements, compounds, mixtures; physical and chemical changes; acids and bases; atomic structure **Theme:** *Scale*
	**UNIT D Magnetism and Electricity** Properties of magnets; forms of electrical energy; electric circuits; sources of electric current; how electric current is changed into useful energy **Theme:** *Models*	**UNIT F Light and Sound** Properties of light; lenses and their uses; color; properties of sound; the sense of hearing; controlling, recording, and transmitting sound **Theme:** *Models*	**UNIT F Forces and Motion** Characteristics of motion; gravity; measuring changes in motion; friction; action-reaction forces; how forces affect the motion of objects **Theme:** *Scale*
UNIT B Sun, Moon, and Earth The physical features of the Sun and Moon; the rotation and revolution of Earth and the Moon; planets of the solar system; Earth's seasonal changes; eclipses **Theme:** *Scale*	**UNIT A Earth's Land** How moving water, wind, and ice shape the land; natural resources and conservation efforts; consequences of producing and disposing of trash **Theme:** *Constancy and Change*	**UNIT B The Solar System and Beyond** The night sky; how astronomers learn about space; the solar system; stars and galaxies; survival in space **Theme:** *Scale*	**UNIT B The Changing Earth** Theory of plate tectonics; the movement of continents; the formation of mountains; earthquakes and volcanoes **Theme:** *Models*
UNIT D Earth's Resources The importance of air, water, and land; renewable, nonrenewable, and inexhaustible resources; uses and protection of Earth's air, water, and land; forces that change Earth's surface; properties of soils **Theme:** *Constancy and Change*	**UNIT E Weather and Climate** Earth's atmosphere; effects of changes in the air on weather; the water cycle; weather patterns and predictions; seasonal weather changes and climate **Theme:** *Constancy and Change*	**UNIT E The Solid Earth** Properties and uses of minerals and rocks; the rock cycle; Earth's structure; fossils as clues to the age of rocks; the formation of crustal features, such as mountains **Theme:** *Constancy and Change*	**UNIT E Oceanography** Contents and properties of ocean water; features and exploration of the ocean floor; currents, waves, and tides; resources from the ocean; ocean pollution **Theme:** *Systems*

TEACHING MODEL

Flexibility is an important feature of the Science DiscoveryWorks *program. Although the* Teaching Guide *suggests ways in which you can use the program components to organize and guide each lesson, you can adapt these suggestions or develop your own teaching strategies. The model shown here is one way of teaching a unit.*

Unit Opener

The *Unit Opener* headline and photograph highlight a scientific phenomenon that occurs in a real-world setting. The opener can be used to engage students' interest in the topic to be studied.

Introduction Have students read the introductory paragraph and discuss what they know about the science topic.

Think Like a Scientist Have students review some of the questions they will investigate in the unit and then have them suggest some of their own questions.

Chapter Opener

The *Chapter Opener* photograph and introductory text focuses on people using science and the role of science in culture and the arts. The photo and text can be used as a discussion starter for the chapter topics.

Warm-up Activity Use the suggested activity in the *Teaching Guide* to motivate interest.

Home-School Connection Extend science learning to the home with easy-to-do activities.

Investigations

The *Investigations*, which form the heart of the **Science DiscoveryWorks** program, are made up of two types of student pages—*Activities* and *Resources*.

Activities Provide hands-on experiences for students that make subsequent readings more meaningful. These experiences form the basis for conceptual development.

- Use the suggested baseline assessment in the *Teaching Guide* to activate prior knowledge.

- Have students record their observations, data, and responses in their *Science Notebooks* as they do the Activities.

- Have students go beyond the basic Activities, using suggestions found in *Investigate Further* boxes. These suggestions include both hands-on and CD-ROM activities.

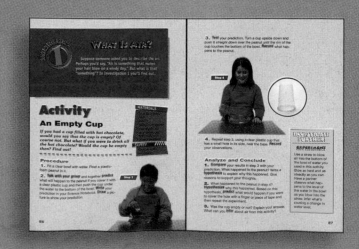

Resources Provide solid science content that reinforces and extends the concepts that students explored in the Activities.

- In addition to regular text material, these resources use a variety of approaches that include Time Capsules; How It Works; Science, Technology & Society; and Global Views.

- Use the *Unit Project Links* and the associated *Science Notebook* pages to provide students with an opportunity to apply their knowledge and understanding.

Close the Investigation Assess student understanding of key science concepts and vocabulary.

- Have students write the answers to the *Think It–Write It* questions in their *Science Notebooks*.

- Use the *Investigation Review* found in the *Ongoing Assessment* section of the *Teacher Resource Book*.

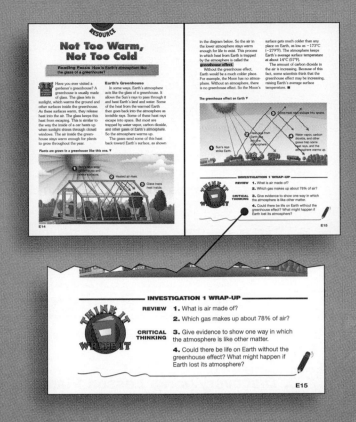

Reflect and Evaluate _____

The *Reflect and Evaluate* page at the end of each chapter helps students reinforce and review the concepts developed in the chapter.

- Have students reflect on their understanding by answering the questions in their *Science Notebooks*.

- Use the *Performance Assessment* suggestion, with accompanying scoring rubric, found in the *Teaching Guide,* to further assess student understanding.

Unit Wrap-up _____

The *Unit Wrap-up* page at the end of each unit reinforces student understanding of the scientific process.

Think Like a Scientist Have students use these suggestions to investigate a question on their own, using scientific methods.

Writing in Science Extend communication skills in a science context.

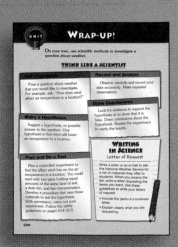

TECHNOLOGY RESOURCES

Science DiscoveryWorks offers a wide variety of technology resources that provide alternative ways of presenting and developing science concepts. These resources also provide students with opportunities to use technological tools and to develop an understanding of how technology contributes to advances in science.

Computer Resources

For the Teacher

DiscoveryWorks Lesson Planner
A lesson planning CD-ROM tool allows you to customize the order of units, choose the lessons you plan to teach, and select the number and lengths of periods taught per week.

DiscoveryWorks Test Generator
This CD-ROM contains ready-made chapter, unit, and standardized-format tests, in English and Spanish, that can be easily customized to meet your needs. Choose from multiple-choice and free-response questions.

For the Student

Science Processor CD-ROM
This software provides an interactive, child-centered learning approach. The CD-ROM provides Investigations that replace or enhance the Investigations in the student book. The software also includes a Science Workshop in which students can explore and create in an open environment, as well as a customized encyclopedia. On-screen tools include a Spreadsheet, a Grapher, a Writer, a Painter, a Calculator, and a Timer.

Best of the Net This CD-ROM program provides guided Internet experiences in Life Science, Earth Science, Physical Science, and the Human Body. It requires no Internet connection.

For the Teacher and the Student

www.eduplace.com Visit Houghton Mifflin's Web site for a rich environment of interactive on-line teacher resources and student activities. Internet Field Trips and Unit Project Links referenced in the Student Edition are supported with up-to-date links. Included are professional and home resources, Kids' Clubhouse science activities, Teacher's Discussion Forums, and an area for classes to share their project results.

Video/Audio Resources

Videotapes "Bill Nye the Science Guy" videos are correlated to units throughout *DiscoveryWorks*. Ways to use these exciting videos to enhance or extend science concepts are suggested on the Using Technology pages that precede each unit.

Activity Video Lab Video demonstrations aid you in preparing, conducting, and concluding activities from *DiscoveryWorks*.

Books on Tape Audiotapes, in English and Spanish, enable students to follow along as the Student Edition is read aloud. These tapes help meet the individual needs of auditory learners, bilingual and ESL students, and challenged readers.

MEETING INDIVIDUAL NEEDS

We know that classroom educators today are very conscious of trying to meet the needs of a diverse student population. Houghton Mifflin Science DiscoveryWorks provides varied activities throughout the program designed to help you meet these needs.

Students Acquiring English

These activities are intended for use with students who are just learning the English language.

Gifted and Talented

These activities are appropriate for students who can think creatively and work independently on more challenging tasks.

Inclusion

These activities are intended for students with mental or physical disabilities who might benefit from alternative learning strategies.

Early Finishers

These activities can be used with students who complete the basic material earlier than the rest of the students.

For Extra Help

These activities provide additional help for students who are having difficulty understanding the concept of the lesson.

Learning Styles

Additionally, we realize that learning styles vary from student to student and even vary for a given student on different topics. Therefore, we have provided Activities that use the following learning styles to enable students to learn in ways that are most comfortable to them.

- LINGUISTIC
- VISUAL/SPATIAL
- LOGICAL/MATHEMATICAL
- KINESTHETIC
- AUDITORY

CONCEPT MAPS

Helping Students Organize Data

Houghton Mifflin *Science DiscoveryWorks* uses concept maps throughout the program to help students identify, organize, and process science information. These maps can be used to enhance student understanding by presenting processes and relationships visually.

KWL Chart

KWL charts help students form purposes for reading. The name of the concept being studied goes at the top of the chart. The first column is for recording what students know about the concept, and the second column is for recording what they want to know about it. In the last column, students record what they've learned after they have completed the unit.

Topic	The Solar System		
K What you know	**W** What you want to know	**L** What you learned
Earth revolves around the Sun. There are other planets in our solar system.	What are the other planets? Do other planets have moons?	

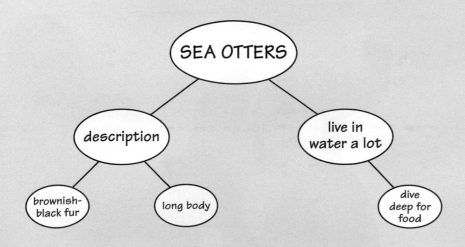

Webs

Webs can be used to show main ideas and subordinate ideas as well as part-whole relationships. The central large circle is for showing the main idea or concept. Smaller circles are for showing subordinate ideas.

Venn Diagram

A Venn diagram is an excellent way to compare and contrast things, such as a robin and a cardinal. Characteristics both birds share, such as wings and feathers, are listed in the overlapping parts of the two circles. Unique characteristics are listed in the non-overlapping parts of the circles.

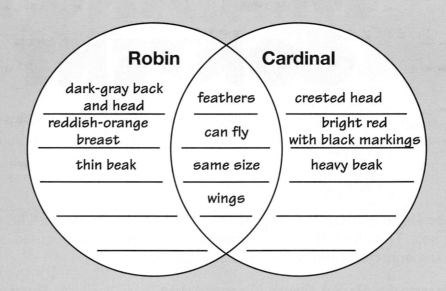

Robin: dark-gray back and head, reddish-orange breast, thin beak

Both: feathers, can fly, same size, wings

Cardinal: crested head, bright red with black markings, heavy beak

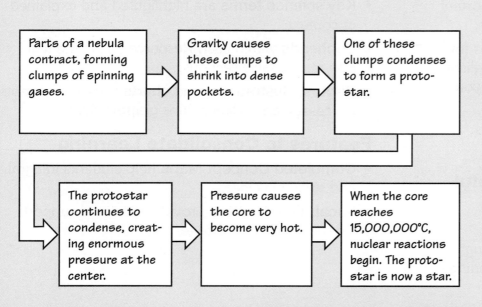

Parts of a nebula contract, forming clumps of spinning gases. → Gravity causes these clumps to shrink into dense pockets. → One of these clumps condenses to form a proto-star. → The protostar continues to condense, creating enormous pressure at the center. → Pressure causes the core to become very hot. → When the core reaches 15,000,000°C, nuclear reactions begin. The proto-star is now a star.

Sequence Chart

A sequence chart can be used to clarify the steps of a process or a chain of events. Each step is recorded in its own box, and the boxes are connected by arrows. In some cases, the last step in a process leads back to the first step. The chart then becomes a representation of a cycle.

Cause and Effect

A cause-and-effect chart shows the relationship between causes and effects. Sometimes you may want to show how multiple causes lead to one effect. At other times you may want to show how one cause leads to several effects. You may also want to show a chain of causes and effects.

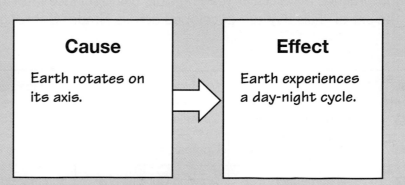

Cause

Earth rotates on its axis.

Effect

Earth experiences a day-night cycle.

READING IN THE CONTENT AREA

Houghton Mifflin's Science DiscoveryWorks *helps make science concepts and informational text accessible to all students by providing students with opportunities to practice and apply reading skills and strategies.*

Improving Reading Comprehension

Science DiscoveryWorks recognizes that students can sometimes have difficulty reading informational text. Therefore, the development of *DiscoveryWorks* focused on creating a program that helps students read purposefully and strategically.

Features to Build Prior Knowledge

- **Concept Map Transparencies** preview important chapter ideas and their relationships.
- **Support Terms** (words that present problems for some students, especially those acquiring English) are identified in the *Teaching Guide* so that you can help students before they begin reading.
- **Concrete Hands-on Activities** help students understand concepts before they read.

Features to Make Reading Purposeful

- **KWL Activities** at the start of each unit help students inquire as they read and study.
- The **Reading Focus** question at the beginning of each Resource helps set a purpose for reading.

Features to Maximize Comprehension

- **Key science terms** are highlighted and explained in context.
- **Subheads** within each Resource divide the text into manageable sections.
- **Photos, illustrations,** and **charts** present concepts, processes, and relationships graphically.

Features to Consolidate Learning

- **Completed Concept Maps** help students integrate and study new ideas.
- **Vocabulary Masters** provide additional support for the chapter science terms.

Using Reading Skills Pages

At the end of each unit, a *Using Reading Skills* page gives students an additional opportunity to apply and practice a particular reading skill, using science informational text. The table below shows the set of skills that are developed across Grades 3 through 6 in *Science DiscoveryWorks*.

Unit	Grade 3	Grade 4	Grade 5	Grade 6
Unit A	Finding the Main Idea	Main Idea and Details	Main Idea and Details	Detecting the Sequence
Unit B	Drawing Conclusions	Cause and Effect	Drawing Conclusions	Main Idea and Details
Unit C	Detecting the Sequence	Compare and Contrast	Cause and Effect	Drawing Conclusions
Unit D	Cause and Effect	Drawing Conclusions	Summarizing	Cause and Effect
Unit E	Compare and Contrast	Detecting the Sequence	Detecting the Sequence	Compare and Contrast
Unit F			Compare and Contrast	Summarizing

INTEGRATING SCIENCE & MATH

Since mathematics frequently supports or forms the basis for scientific ideas, students often use their math skills as they study science. Science DiscoveryWorks, therefore, provides a variety of opportunities for students to apply, practice, and improve their math skills and knowledge.

Applying and Practicing Math Skills

It is often helpful to know exactly where math can be found in a science lesson. The icons below, which appear in the Student Edition, will help you and your students see and better use the connections that naturally exist between science and math.

Using Math You will find the *Using Math* feature throughout the Resources. This feature is usually a special "math caption" that asks students to use the data presented in drawings, graphs, or other visuals. For example, students may be asked to use computational skills, compare data, estimate, and apply other math skills.

Math Hint This feature is found throughout the Activities. These hints are included in procedural steps in Activities to assist students with the math that is needed in order to do the Activity successfully.

Science and Math Toolbox This section of the Student Edition provides instruction in using science equipment and reviews the math skills that are needed to do the Activities successfully. The Science and Math Toolbox varies by grade level so that skills and tools may be introduced at the appropriate time. Students can use these pages to review measurement techniques, graphs, calculators, and other skills and tools. The Toolbox is referenced in Activities where a particular skill or tool is needed.

Using Math Skills Pages

At the end of each unit, a *Using Math Skills* page gives students an additional opportunity to apply and practice a particular math skill in the context of science content. The table below shows the set of skills that are developed across Grades 3 through 6 in *Science DiscoveryWorks*.

Unit	Grade 3	Grade 4	Grade 5	Grade 6
Unit A	Analyze Data	Circle Graph	Line Graph	Analyze Data
Unit B	Time Measurement	Volume	Analyze Data	Bar Graph
Unit C	Bar Graph	Analyze Data	Equations and Formulas	Line Graph
Unit D	Circle Graph	Bar Graph	Circle Graph	Analyze Data
Unit E	Analyze Data	Line Graph	Bar Graph	Circle Graph
Unit F			Analyze Data	Equations and Formulas

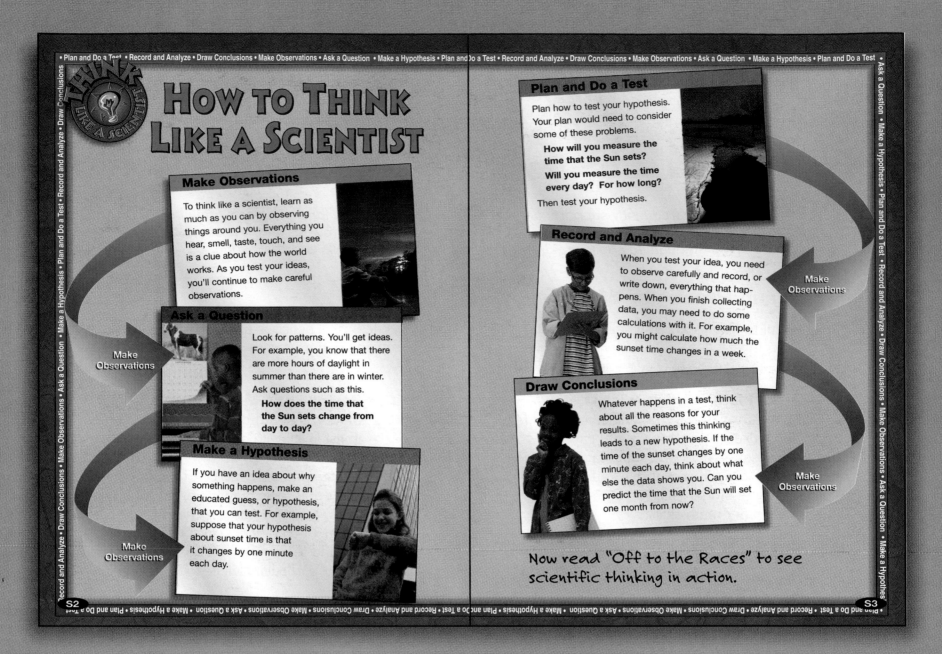

HOW TO THINK LIKE A SCIENTIST

Make Observations

To think like a scientist, learn as much as you can by observing things around you. Everything you hear, smell, taste, touch, and see is a clue about how the world works. As you test your ideas, you'll continue to make careful observations.

Ask a Question

Look for patterns. You'll get ideas. For example, you know that there are more hours of daylight in summer than there are in winter. Ask questions such as this.

How does the time that the Sun sets change from day to day?

Make a Hypothesis

If you have an idea about why something happens, make an educated guess, or hypothesis, that you can test. For example, suppose that your hypothesis about sunset time is that it changes by one minute each day.

Plan and Do a Test

Plan how to test your hypothesis. Your plan would need to consider some of these problems.

How will you measure the time that the Sun sets?

Will you measure the time every day? For how long?

Then test your hypothesis.

Record and Analyze

When you test your idea, you need to observe carefully and record, or write down, everything that happens. When you finish collecting data, you may need to do some calculations with it. For example, you might calculate how much the sunset time changes in a week.

Draw Conclusions

Whatever happens in a test, think about all the reasons for your results. Sometimes this thinking leads to a new hypothesis. If the time of the sunset changes by one minute each day, think about what else the data shows you. Can you predict the time that the Sun will set one month from now?

Now read "Off to the Races" to see scientific thinking in action.

HOW DO SCIENTISTS STUDY NATURE?

What discoveries and inventions have had the greatest impact on people's lives? Antibiotics? Cell biology? The structure of matter? The printing press? Computer technology? Although all of these would be nominated, most people would not identify scientific thinking as a great invention. Yet this unique process for building knowledge has led to many discoveries. What makes this process such a powerful tool?

Exploring Nature

Until the seventeenth century, most people accepted untested explanations of events in nature. Myths and superstitions were often part of such explanations. Most people thought that Earth was at the center of the universe. They believed that the Sun, Moon, planets, and stars circled Earth. Although some scientists had hypothesized that Earth circled the Sun, it took an invention—the telescope—and the inquiring

mind of a great scientist, Galileo Galilei, to provide evidence that supported this hypothesis.

Scientific Revolution

In 1609, Galileo peered through his primitive telescope at the planet Jupiter and *observed* what appeared to be tiny "stars" in a straight line near the giant planet. As he studied the planet for many nights, he was amazed to discover that the stars moved, yet stayed close to Jupiter. He *questioned* what these points of light could be. After *recording* the position of the stars each night and *analyzing* his records, Galileo *concluded* that the tiny lights must be Jupiter's moons. Galileo's discovery contradicted the common thinking of the day—that all heavenly bodies orbited Earth. And his evidence paved the way for popular acceptance of a revolutionary new way of understanding nature—scientific thinking.

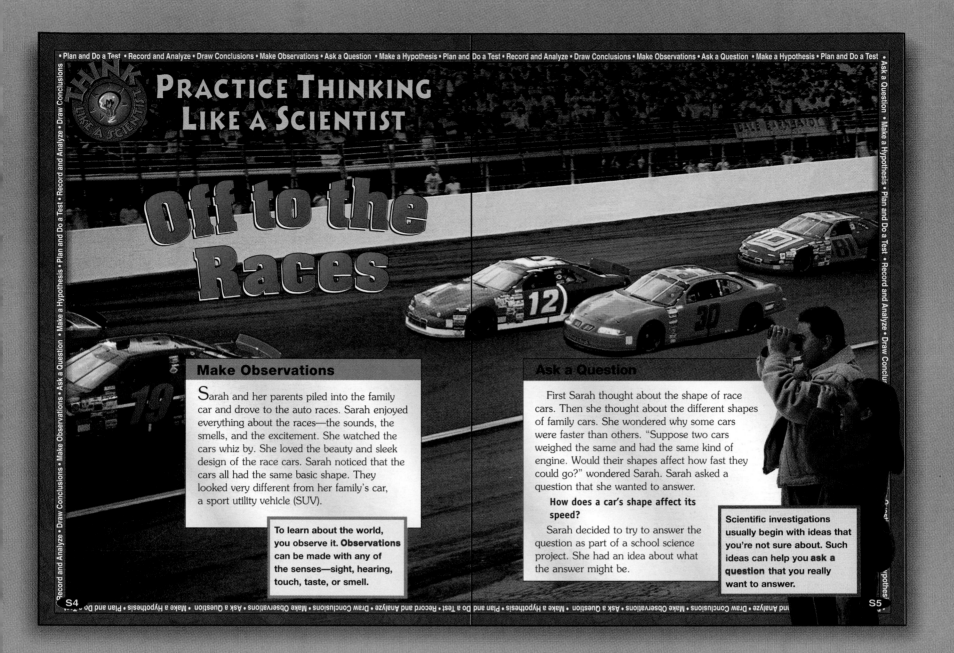

PRACTICE THINKING LIKE A SCIENTIST

Off to the Races

Make Observations

Sarah and her parents piled into the family car and drove to the auto races. Sarah enjoyed everything about the races—the sounds, the smells, and the excitement. She watched the cars whiz by. She loved the beauty and sleek design of the race cars. Sarah noticed that the cars all had the same basic shape. They looked very different from her family's car, a sport utility vehicle (SUV).

To learn about the world, you observe it. **Observations** can be made with any of the senses—sight, hearing, touch, taste, or smell.

Ask a Question

First Sarah thought about the shape of race cars. Then she thought about the different shapes of family cars. She wondered why some cars were faster than others. "Suppose two cars weighed the same and had the same kind of engine. Would their shapes affect how fast they could go?" wondered Sarah. Sarah asked a question that she wanted to answer.

How does a car's shape affect its speed?

Sarah decided to try to answer the question as part of a school science project. She had an idea about what the answer might be.

Scientific investigations usually begin with ideas that you're not sure about. Such ideas can help you **ask a question** that you really want to answer.

WHAT IS SCIENTIFIC THINKING?

Scientific thinking, also commonly called "scientific inquiry" or "the scientific method," is not a single method with a set number of orderly steps. It is a flexible process for both asking and answering questions about nature. Scientific thinking involves:

- Using all of the senses to make careful observations

- Asking specific questions about those observations that can be answered by using the tools of science

- Forming hypotheses that explain what is observed

- Testing these hypotheses through experiments and other tests and gathering and recording data

- Analyzing and drawing conclusions from the data

- Asking new questions, making new observations, and forming new hypotheses based on those findings

In school, students can learn how to use the process of scientific thinking in their daily lives. Students can also discover the vast body of knowledge that scientists, using that same process, have uncovered.

Scientific inquiry is dependent on critical-thinking skills. Scientists analyze nature in their attempts to understand and explain how nature works. This often involves breaking a phenomenon down (mentally and physically) into smaller and smaller parts to understand how the parts relate. Scientists also employ synthesis in their work—putting together pieces of the puzzle that is nature.

Scientific thinking also involves keeping an open mind about ideas. A tendency to want to investigate for oneself, rather than to accept the explanations of others, also characterizes scientific thinking.

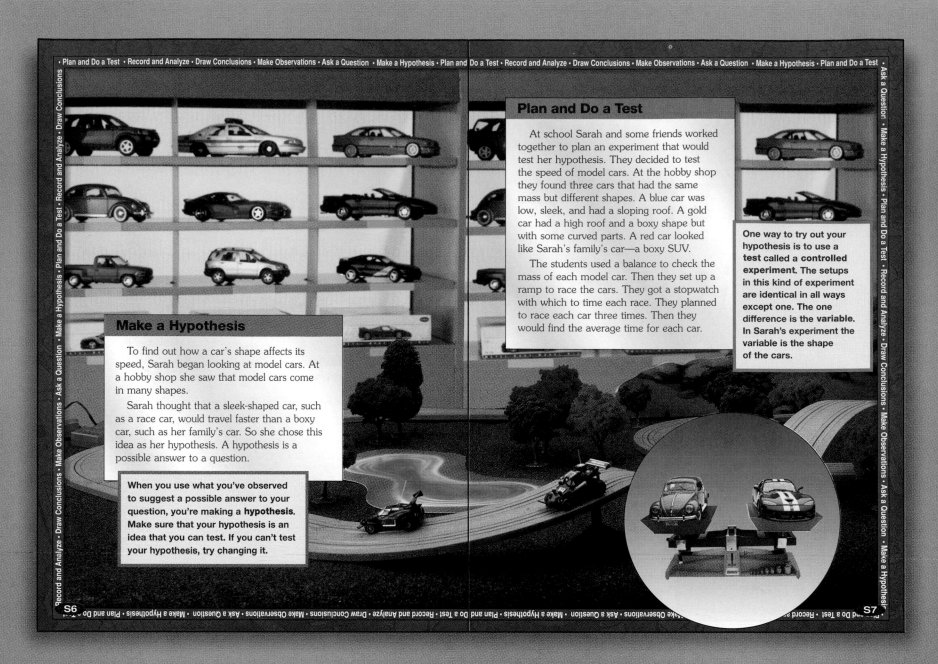

WHERE IS THE EVIDENCE?

With which of the following statements would your students agree? *Friday the 13th is an unlucky day. In a championship game, the home team has an advantage. Studying with the television on doesn't affect learning. If five coin tosses in a row show heads, the next toss is more likely to be tails.* To a scientist, each of these statements can be considered a testable *hypothesis.*

Gathering Data

Which hypotheses are supported by evidence and which are just unsupported opinions? There are many ways to test a hypothesis. Some involve gathering data and analyzing it. For example, is Friday the 13th really an "unlucky" day? A scientist would start by carefully defining certain terms and gathering information. What does the word *unlucky* mean in measurable terms? How many times has Friday occurred on the 13th of the month? Are there more unlucky events on Friday the 13th than on the 13th day of the month when that day doesn't land on a Friday? By analyzing this data, a scientist could draw reasonable conclusions about whether the data supported the hypothesis that Friday the 13th was "unlucky."

A Controlled Test

Sometimes a hypothesis is best tested in a carefully controlled experiment. To discover if studying with the television on affects grades, scientists would compare students' learning scores under two conditions—an experimental condition in which the television is on and a control condition in which it is not. Again, data would be gathered and analyzed to determine if the hypothesis is supported or not. And the experiment would be repeated to verify the results.

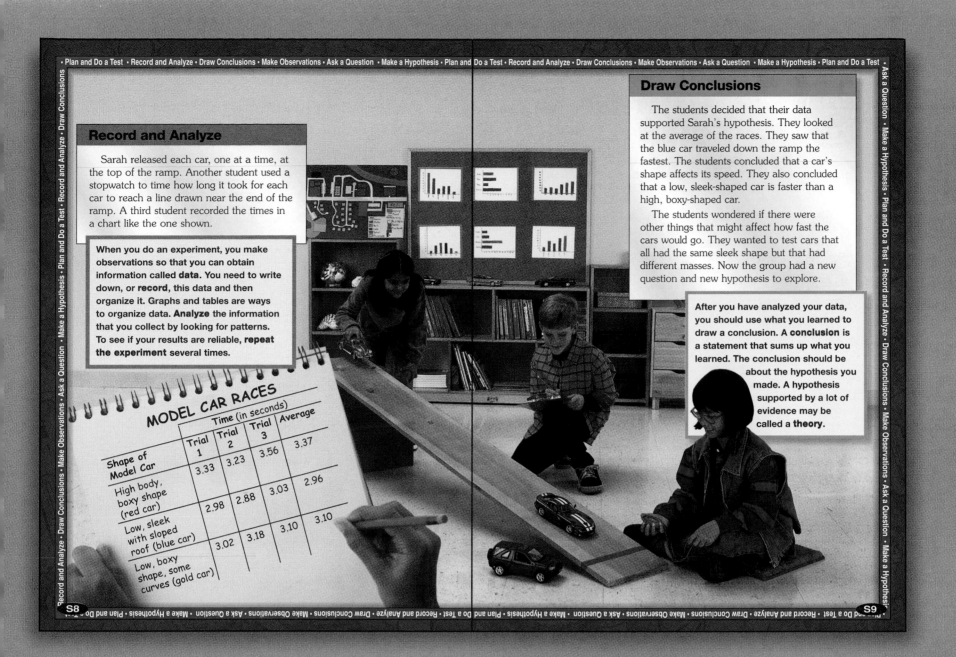

Record and Analyze

Sarah released each car, one at a time, at the top of the ramp. Another student used a stopwatch to time how long it took for each car to reach a line drawn near the end of the ramp. A third student recorded the times in a chart like the one shown.

When you do an experiment, you make observations so that you can obtain information called **data**. You need to write down, or **record**, this data and then organize it. Graphs and tables are ways to organize data. **Analyze** the information that you collect by looking for patterns. To see if your results are reliable, **repeat the experiment** several times.

Draw Conclusions

The students decided that their data supported Sarah's hypothesis. They looked at the average of the races. They saw that the blue car traveled down the ramp the fastest. The students concluded that a car's shape affects its speed. They also concluded that a low, sleek-shaped car is faster than a high, boxy-shaped car.

The students wondered if there were other things that might affect how fast the cars would go. They wanted to test cars that all had the same sleek shape but that had different masses. Now the group had a new question and new hypothesis to explore.

After you have analyzed your data, you should use what you learned to draw a conclusion. A **conclusion** is a statement that sums up what you learned. The conclusion should be about the hypothesis you made. A hypothesis supported by a lot of evidence may be called a **theory**.

MODEL CAR RACES

Shape of Model Car	Time (in seconds)			
	Trial 1	Trial 2	Trial 3	Average
High body, boxy shape (red car)	3.33	3.23	3.56	3.37
Low, sleek with sloped roof (blue car)	2.98	2.88	3.03	2.96
Low, boxy shape, some curves (gold car)	3.02	3.18	3.10	3.10

HOW DO SCIENTISTS BUILD KNOWLEDGE?

The power of scientific thinking becomes evident when scientists share their data, analyses, and results at national and international meetings and in specialized science journals. This communication and teamwork is important because it serves as a way to collect and disseminate scientific findings. Because scientists may draw different conclusions from the same data, it also allows other scientists to challenge, retest, and verify or refute the findings of other researchers.

Scientific Theories

When a hypothesis about natural phenomena is strongly supported by evidence and widely accepted by the scientific community, the hypothesis is called a *theory*. A theory usually explains a broader range of phenomena than does a hypothesis. Also, a theory often includes a demonstrable model of how ideas fit together. New theories can replace older ones as more data is gathered. For example, Copernicus's theory of a heliocentric (Sun-centered) universe replaced Ptolemy's geocentric (Earth-centered) theory when Galileo and others demonstrated conclusively that all objects in the universe did not orbit Earth.

Scientific Laws

Descriptions of natural phenomena are referred to as *scientific laws*. Such descriptions are often mathematical and have great predictive value. Sir Isaac Newton's laws of motion and law of universal gravitation are examples of scientific laws.

USING SCIENCE PROCESS SKILLS

Observing involves gathering information about the environment through your five senses—seeing, hearing, smelling, touching, and tasting.

Classifying is grouping objects or events according to common properties or characteristics. Often you can classify in more than one way.

Measuring and using numbers involves the ability to make measurements (including time measurements), to make estimates, and to record data.

Communicating involves using words, both speaking and writing, and using actions, graphs, tables, diagrams, and other ways of presenting information.

Inferring means coming to a conclusion based on facts and observations you've made.

Predicting involves stating in advance what you think will happen based on observations and experiences.

Collecting, recording, and interpreting data all involve gathering and understanding information. This skill includes organizing data in tables, graphs, and in other ways. Interpretation includes finding patterns and relationships that lead to new questions and new ideas.

Identifying and controlling variables involves determining the effect of a changing factor, called the variable, in an experiment. To do this, you keep all other factors constant, or unchanging.

Defining operationally means to describe an object, an event, or an idea based on personal observations. An operational definition of a plant might be that it is a green living thing that is attached to soil and that does not move around.

Making a hypothesis is suggesting a possible answer to a question or making an educated guess about why something happens. Your hypothesis should be based on observations and experiences.

Experimenting is testing your hypothesis to collect evidence that supports the hypothesis or shows that it is false.

Making and using models includes designing and making physical models of processes and objects, or making mental models to represent objects and ideas.

HOW CAN SCIENTIFIC THINKING BE APPLIED?

The importance of learning to think scientifically beginning in elementary school cannot be underestimated. Every aspect of home and career in the twenty-first century will require students to apply science process skills. The following activities can be used throughout the year to reinforce the wealth of opportunities *Science DiscoveryWorks* integrates into each Investigation.

Testing Ideas

On a self-stick note or on an index card, have each student write a science question he or she is curious about but can't answer. Have each student describe an observation that prompted the question. On a bulletin board, arrange the notes in the shape of a large question mark. Divide the students into groups. Ask each group to select a question that students in the group think they already know something about or one they

are confident they can answer with a little library research or experimentation. Explain that each group must write a testable hypothesis to answer the question and identify the science process skills they would need to use in answering it. Encourage them to list other questions that occur to them.

What's the Best Money Can Buy?

What brands of supplies should your school purchase? Have students apply science process skills, beginning with observations and questions they have about the supplies they use in school each day, such as crayons, paper, pencils, washroom soap, paper towels and so on. Ask students to choose a product, ask questions about it, and design tests to compare it to other brands. Provide an opportunity to submit the findings to school administrators and board members.

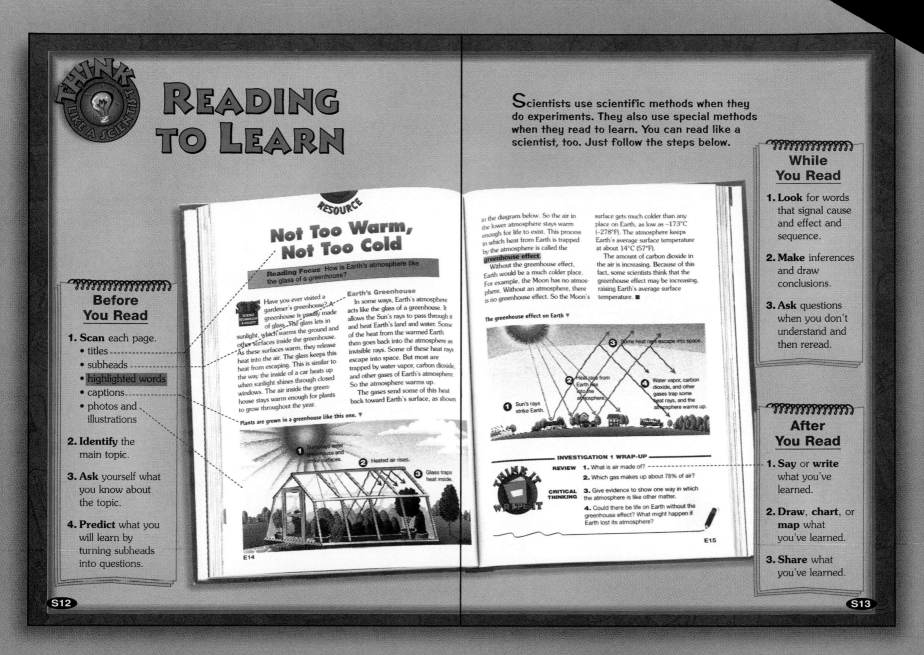

READING TO LEARN

Scientists use scientific methods when they do experiments. They also use special methods when they read to learn. You can read like a scientist, too. Just follow the steps below.

Before You Read

1. **Scan** each page.
   • titles
   • subheads
   • highlighted words
   • captions
   • photos and illustrations

2. **Identify** the main topic.

3. **Ask** yourself what you know about the topic.

4. **Predict** what you will learn by turning subheads into questions.

While You Read

1. **Look** for words that signal cause and effect and sequence.

2. **Make** inferences and draw conclusions.

3. **Ask** questions when you don't understand and then reread.

After You Read

1. **Say** or **write** what you've learned.

2. **Draw**, **chart**, or **map** what you've learned.

3. **Share** what you've learned.

Not Too Warm, Not Too Cold

Reading Focus How is Earth's atmosphere like the glass of a greenhouse?

Have you ever visited a gardener's greenhouse? A greenhouse is usually made of glass. The glass lets in sunlight, which warms the ground and other surfaces inside the greenhouse. As these surfaces warm, they release heat into the air. The glass keeps this heat from escaping. This is similar to the way the inside of a car heats up when sunlight shines through closed windows. The air inside the greenhouse stays warm enough for plants to grow throughout the year.

Earth's Greenhouse

In some ways, Earth's atmosphere acts like the glass of a greenhouse. It allows the Sun's rays to pass through it and heat Earth's land and water. Some of the heat from the warmed Earth then goes back into the atmosphere as invisible rays. Some of these heat rays escape into space. But most are trapped by water vapor, carbon dioxide, and other gases of Earth's atmosphere. So the atmosphere warms up.

The gases send some of this heat back toward Earth's surface, as shown in the diagram below. So the air in the lower atmosphere stays warm enough for life to exist. This process in which heat from Earth is trapped by the atmosphere is called the **greenhouse effect**.

Without the greenhouse effect, Earth would be a much colder place. For example, the Moon has no atmosphere. Without an atmosphere, there is no greenhouse effect. So the Moon's surface gets much colder than any place on Earth, as low as –173°C (–278°F). The atmosphere keeps Earth's average surface temperature at about 14°C (57°F).

The amount of carbon dioxide in the air is increasing. Because of this fact, some scientists think that the greenhouse effect may be increasing, raising Earth's average surface temperature. ■

Plants are grown in a greenhouse like this one. ▼

1 Sun's rays enter greenhouse and strike surfaces.
2 Heated air rises.
3 Glass traps heat inside.

E14

The greenhouse effect on Earth ▼

1 Sun's rays strike Earth.
2 Heat rays from Earth rise into the atmosphere.
3 Some heat rays escape into space.
4 Water vapor, carbon dioxide, and other gases trap some heat rays, and the atmosphere warms up.

INVESTIGATION 1 WRAP-UP

REVIEW
1. What is air made of?
2. Which gas makes up about 78% of air?

CRITICAL THINKING
3. Give evidence to show one way in which the atmosphere is like other matter.
4. Could there be life on Earth without the greenhouse effect? What might happen if Earth lost its atmosphere?

E15

S12 • S13

READING TO LEARN

Before Students Read

Discuss each numbered feature with students and explain how each will help them read more effectively.

• Guide students to preview the reading by scanning titles and heads.

• Have students use the Reading Focus question to set a purpose for reading.

• Point out that asking questions helps students engage their interest in the topic.

• Suggest that students look ahead at illustrations and captions to predict what they will find in the reading.

While Students Read

Explain how the numbered strategies can help students while they read.

• Show students how signal words like *first*, *next*, *so*, and *because* identify important relationships such as sequence and cause and effect.

• Help students draw conclusions and make inferences by thinking about what they are reading.

• Have students self-monitor their reading by asking themselves questions as they read.

After Students Read

Encourage students to review what they have read and to assess their understanding by using these strategies.

• Have students restate or write down main ideas and important details to help remember information.

• Show students how using graphic aids such as charts or diagrams help them organize information.

• Point out that sharing what they read helps students summarize what they have read.

SAFETY

The best way to be safe in the classroom and outdoors is to use common sense. Prepare for each activity before you start it. Get help from your teacher when there is a problem. Always pay attention.

Stay Safe From Stains
- Wear protective clothing or an old shirt when you work with messy materials.
- If anything spills, wipe it up or ask your teacher to help you clean it up.

Stay Safe From Flames
- Keep your clothes away from open flames. If you have long or baggy sleeves, roll them up.
- Don't let your hair get close to a flame. If you have long hair, tie it back.

Make Wise Choices About Materials
- Use only the amount of material you need.
- Recycle materials so they can be reused.
- Take care when using valuable tools so they can be used again.

Stay Safe From Injuries

- Protect your eyes by wearing safety goggles when you are told that you need them.
- Keep your hands dry around electricity. Water is a good conductor of electricity, so you can get a shock more easily if your hands are wet.
- Be careful with sharp objects. If you have to press on them, keep the sharp side away from you.
- Cover any cuts you have that are exposed. If you spill something on a cut, be sure to wash it off immediately.
- Don't eat or drink anything unless your teacher tells you that it's okay.

Stay Safe During Cleanup
- Wash up after you finish working.
- Dispose of things in the way that your teacher tells you to.

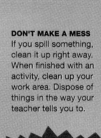

S14

HAIR Keep it out of the way of a flame.

EYES Wear safety goggles when you are told to.

MOUTH Don't eat or drink ANYTHING unless your teacher tells you it's okay.

CLOTHES Keep long, loose sleeves rolled up. Protect your clothes from stains. Stay away from open flames.

HANDS Keep your hands dry around electricity. Cover any cuts. Wear gloves when told to. Wash up after you finish.

DON'T MAKE A MESS If you spill something, clean it up right away. When finished with an activity, clean up your work area. Dispose of things in the way your teacher tells you to.

MOST IMPORTANTLY If you ever hurt yourself, or one of your group members gets hurt, tell your teacher right away.

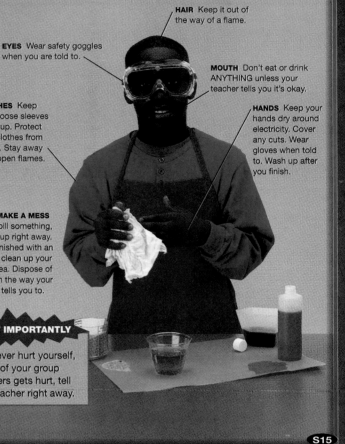

S15

SAFETY

In order for students to develop respect for safety, they need to understand exactly what is meant by safe and unsafe behavior and what the rationale is behind safety rules. Through your teaching, students can develop the "safe science" attitudes and skills that are essential both in school and at home.

General Safety Guidelines

- Post an easy-to-read list of safety rules in a prominent place in the classroom. Review it with students on a regular basis.
- Become familiar with the safety procedures that are necessary for each activity before introducing it to your students.
- Discuss specific safety precautions with students before beginning every hands-on science activity.
- Always act as an exemplary model of safe behavior.
- Have students wear protective aprons, goggles, and gloves whenever these items will prevent injury.
- Keep safety equipment, such as extinguishers, readily accessible and know how to use it.
- Prepare students for emergencies by having them practice leaving the classroom quickly and safely.
- Show students how to obtain help in an emergency by using the telephone, an intercom, or other available means of communication.
- Never leave students unattended while they are involved in science activities.
- Provide ample space for activities that require students to move about and handle materials.
- Keep your classroom and all science materials in proper condition. Check their condition regularly.
- Tell students to report injuries to you immediately.

UNIT D

Magnetism and Electricity

Overview Magnetism and Electricity explores the properties of magnets and the behavior of electric charges in both static and current electricity. Through the resources and activities, students investigate how magnets pull on things made of iron without touching them, act through other materials, and exert a push or a pull on other magnets. Students also discover that electrically charged materials exert a push or pull on other objects. They investigate electric current by creating series and parallel circuits and devices such as electric cells and electromagnets. Finally, students examine how electric power is generated and transported and focus on electrical safety.

Theme Models is the theme that unites the major concepts of Magnetism and Electricity. Once students are familiar with the elements of a magnetic system, Earth's magnetic field is compared with that of the familiar bar magnet. Students next use conceptual models to understand the flow of electricity through a wire by comparing it with the flow of water in a hose. Learning about some of the simple relations between magnets and electric current, students will broaden their understanding of these fundamental forces of nature.

THE BIG IDEA

Magnetism and electrical energy are related; a magnetic field can produce electricity, and electric current can produce a magnetic field.

Tracing Major Concepts

Magnets and the magnetic force fields around them have observable properties.

Subconcepts

- Magnets attract certain materials such as iron and steel; magnets have north and south poles.

- Magnets have magnetic fields that exert forces in all directions around the magnet.

There are two forms of electrical energy—static and current.

Subconcepts

- Static electricity consists of an electric charge on the surface of an object.

- Current electricity is the flow of negative charges through a conductor in a closed circuit.

- Electric circuits can be put together in series or in parallel.

Electric current is produced in generators, electric cells, and solar cells, and it can be changed into useful forms of energy.

Subconcepts

- Electric current sources include generators, electric cells, and solar cells.

- Electrical energy is changed into useful forms of energy in electric devices.

CONTENTS

Magnetism and Electricity ...D1

THINK LIKE A SCIENTIST

CHAPTER **1**

Magnetism   D4

CHAPTER **2**

Electrical Energy   D26

CHAPTER 3

Electricity at Work   D54

DiscoveryWorks CORRELATIONS

1. Electricity in circuits can produce light, heat, sound, and magnetic effects. Electrical circuits require a complete loop through which an electrical current can pass. *(Ch. 2, Inv. 2 and 3)*

2. Magnets attract and repel each other and certain kinds of other materials. *(Ch. 1)*

3. People have always had questions about their world. Science is one way of answering questions and explaining the natural world. *(Entire Unit)*

4. Safety and security are basic needs of humans. Safety involves freedom from danger, risk, or injury. Security involves feelings of confidence and lack of anxiety and fear. Student understandings include following

safety rules for home and school, preventing abuse and neglect, avoiding injury, knowing whom to ask for help, and when and how to say no. *(Ch. 3, Inv. 2)*

5. Men and women have made a variety of contributions throughout the history of science and technology. *(Entire Unit)*

1. Technology extends the ability of people to change the world: to cut, shape, or put together materials; to move things from one place to another; and to reach farther with their hands, voices, and minds. The changes may be for survival needs such as food, shelter, and defense, for communication and transportation, or to gain knowledge and express ideas. *(Entire Unit)*

2. Without touching them, a magnet pulls on all things made of iron and either pushes or pulls on other magnets. *(Ch. 1; Ch. 3, Inv. 2)*

3. Without touching them, material that has been electrically charged pulls on all other materials and may either push or pull other charged materials. *(Ch. 2, Inv. 1)*

4. Moving air and water can be used to run machines. *(Ch. 3, Inv. 1)*

5. People have invented devices, such as paper and ink, engraved plastic disks, and magnetic tapes, for recording information. These devices enable great amounts of information to be stored and retrieved—and be sent to one or many other people or places. *(Ch. 3, Inv. 2)*

6. Communication technologies make it possible to send and receive information more and more reliably, quickly, and cheaply over long distances. *(Ch. 3, Inv. 2)*

NSES Standards are based on *National Science Education Standards* (© 1996) published by The National Research Council.
Project 2061 Benchmarks are based on *Benchmarks for Science Literacy* (© 1993) published by The American Association for the Advancement of Science.

CURRICULUM INTEGRATION

An integrated approach to the teaching of science will help students understand how science connects to other school subjects as well as to technology and to literature. The chart below indicates where to find the activities in this unit that connect to other disciplines.

THE SCIENCES

- Earth Science, page D11
- Earth Science, page D14
- Life Science, page D21
- Life Science, page D41
- Life Science, page D58

LITERATURE

- *Magnets: Mind-boggling Experiments You Can Turn Into Science Fair Projects*, page D12
- *Hello! Hello! A Look Inside the Telephone*, pages D51, D72

MATH

- Graphing, page D42
- Estimating, page D72

WRITING

- Writing Stories, page D30
- Writing an Ad, page D48
- Researching, page D51
- Write Ad Copy, page D60

CONNECTING SCIENCE TO

SCIENCE AROUND THE WORLD

- Using Maps, page D23
- Aswan Dam, page D40

SOCIAL STUDIES

- Testing, page D12
- Mapping, page D22
- Storm Safety, page D34
- Life Long Ago, page D59
- Electric Inventor, page D70
- Safety First, page D75

TECHNOLOGY & SOCIETY

- Research, page D19
- Inventing, page D31
- Experimenting, page D50
- Energy Sources, page D62
- Electric Cars, page D73

THE ARTS

- Illustrating, page D32
- Acting Out a Skit, page D47
- Draw Designs, page D64
- Design Signs, page D74

Nature's Light and Sound Show

by Betty Preece

Betty Preece is an engineer and a physicist who currently teaches science.

ELECTRICAL STORMS

Thunderstorms are local storms that are accompanied always by lightning and thunder, often by strong winds and heavy rains, and sometimes by hail and tornadoes. At any one time on Earth about 2,000 thunderstorms can exist, producing about 100 lightning flashes each second.

Thunderstorms are notorious for their potential destruction. In the United States alone, lightning causes 100 to 200 deaths, several hundred million dollars in property damage, and over 10,000 forest fires each year.

When Earth's atmosphere becomes unstable, and warm, moist air rises, small, fair-weather cumulus clouds form. As a number of these clouds increase in size and energy, they combine to form large cumulonimbus clouds, with their distinctive anvil-shaped tops. These clouds contain charged particles that result in lightning and thunder.

Regions of charged particles occur within cumulonimbus clouds, with the tops being positively charged and the bases negatively charged. These strong electric fields cause the surrounding air to become ionized, or electrically charged; lightning follows along the conductive paths formed.

Many lightning strokes occur within clouds and are therefore not seen. The most familiar lightning strokes are cloud-to-ground flashes. Because Earth conducts electricity, the negative electrical field of the clouds attracts positive charges on Earth, especially at such locations as tall buildings and trees.

Negative cloud-to-ground flashes start as a downward flow of electric charge called the leader. The leader is thought to be initiated by a small discharge at the cloud base that releases electrons, which are negatively charged, that move toward the ground. When the leader gets within 100 m (330 ft) of Earth, an upward connecting discharge moves up from the ground—especially from buildings and trees. Once these two make contact, the visible lightning stroke, called the return stroke, moves upward from the ground to the cloud.

This process may repeat several times, until the negative charge at the ground is lowered or a positive charge is deposited in the cloud. The heating and expansion of air along the leader path produces the shock wave heard as thunder.

In this cloud-to-ground lightning flash, negative ▶ electric charges in the cloud attract positive charges on the ground and the tree.

TIPS FROM Teachers

Try This!

Teachers and students alike are fascinated by electrical homework-helpers. Let your students make games out of simple circuit boards that will help them study other subjects. Supply brass fasteners, wire, light bulbs, and index cards to make the games. Students can write in the terminology they choose, such as states and state capitals, multiplication facts and answers, characters and character traits, or even lines from poems. Students move markers around the circuit and respond to a question when they stop at a given place. Each circuit board can become a quiz for another student to take.

Beverly Hanrahan
Souderton,
Pennsylvania

Try This!

Hands-on exploration helps prepare students to talk about concepts. For example, before I get into teaching the fairly abstract idea of magnetic poles, I give every student five minutes with a pair of magnets they can handle on their own. Then as a class we'll use everybody's observations to help answer a simple question about magnets: "What do magnets do?" Students will readily tell you that magnets stick together and stick to certain other metal things. The second force is not always so obvious, but it leads into an operational definition of poles: "Place where the magnets stick together and push apart."

Cheryl Stephens
Houston, Texas

Try This!

Construct a magnetic field demonstrator and avoid the mess and hazard of handling iron filings. Put filings in a plastic drink container filled with clear vegetable oil. Clean and dry the lid and neck, then apply a sealant to keep the top on permanently. The oil gives you a great three-dimensional display! You may want to experiment with different containers and magnet shapes.

Richard Bollinger
New York City,
New York

SKILLS FOR SCIENTIFIC LITERACY

Science DiscoveryWorks helps students develop scientific literacy by providing activities and resources that challenge students to use process skills, critical thinking skills, and scientific reasoning skills. Students develop process skills as they ask questions and investigate to discover the answers. They develop critical thinking skills and scientific reasoning skills as they respond to thought-provoking questions about their investigations and in on-going assessment.

Science Process Skills

Science process skills provide a framework in which ideas can be conceptualized, tested, and evaluated. The processes listed here are developed through a wide range of hands-on experiences.

Activities	Page	Observing	Classifying	Measuring/ Using Numbers	Communicating	Inferring	Predicting	Collecting, Recording, and Interpreting Data	Identifying and Controlling Variables	Defining Operationally	Making Hypotheses	Experimenting	Making and Using Models
Make a Magnet	D6	•	•		•	•	•				•		
A Magnet's Ends	D8				•	•	•	•		•		•	
Pulling Through	D10	•	•		•	•	•	•		•		•	
Getting Directions	D16	•			•	•		•					•
Picture a Magnet's Force	D18	•			•		•			•			
Charge!	D28	•		•	•		•	•					
On or Off?	D36						•	•	•	•	•	•	
Stop or Go?	D38		•				•	•	•	•		•	
One Type of Circuit	D44				•	•	•	•		•			
Another Type of Circuit	D46				•	•	•	•		•			
Detect a Circuit	D56	•			•	•							•
A Magnetic Source	D57	•			•	•		•		•	•		•
Make It Move	D66			•	•	•	•		•	•			

Critical Thinking Skills

Critical thinking skills are embedded in the questioning strategies throughout the program. The chart below summarizes the processes assessed in the Think It/Write It sections that end each investigation.

Process	Description	D15	D24	D35	D43	D52	D65	D76
Analyzing	Studying something to identify constituent elements or relationships among elements	•	•				•	•
Synthesizing	Using deductive reasoning to pull together key elements	•		•		•	•	•
Evaluating	Reviewing and responding critically to materials, procedures, or ideas and judging them by purposes, standards, or other criteria		•					•
Applying	Using ideas, processes, or skills in new situations	•		•	•		•	•
Generating Ideas	Expressing thoughts that reveal originality, speculation, imagination, a personal perspective, flexibility in thinking, invention, or creativity				•			
Expressing Ideas	Presenting ideas clearly and in logical order, while using language that is appropriate for the audience and occasion						•	•
Solving Problems	Using critical thinking processes to find solutions to a problem		•		•	•		

Scientific Reasoning Skills

Scientific reasoning skills are developed and reinforced through the science process skills and critical thinking skills.

Reasoning Skill	Description
Longing to Know and Understand	The desire to probe, find information, and seek explanations
Questioning of Scientific Assumptions	The tendency to hold open for further verification of presented assumptions, encounters, and ideas
Searching for Data and Its Meaning	The propensity to collect information and to analyze it in context
Demand for Verification	The inclination to repeat and replicate findings and studies
Respect for Logic	The inclination to move from assumptions to testing and data collection to conclusions
Consideration of Premises	The tendency to put into context the reason for a particular point of view
Consideration of Consequences	The tendency to put into perspective the results of a particular point of view
Respect for Historical Contributions	The inclination to understand and learn from the contributions of earlier ideas, studies, events, and so on

ONGOING ASSESSMENT

Houghton Mifflin Science DiscoveryWorks provides a variety of ongoing assessment tools to help you monitor student growth.

Written Reviews and Tests

Written reviews and tests throughout the program help assess student learning.

In the Student Edition
- Analyze & Conclude questions at end of each Activity
- Think It/Write It questions at end of each Investigation
- Reflect & Evaluate questions at end of each chapter

In the Teacher Resource Book
- Investigation Reviews
- Chapter Tests/Unit Tests
- Chapter and Unit Tests in standardized test format

Performance Assessment

Performance Assessment tasks allow students to demonstrate their learning through hands-on activities.

In the Teaching Guide Performance tasks appear at end of specific investigations and end of each chapter.

In the Teacher Resource Book A Unit Performance Task, with accompanying rubric, appears in each unit.

Portfolio Assessment

Portfolios of student work can be used to holistically assess student progress. Portfolio support material is provided in the ongoing Assessment section of the TRB.

In the Student Edition A Portfolio suggestion appears at end of chapter.

In the Teaching Guide Portfolio tasks appear at end of specific investigations.

Chapter 1
Assessment Options

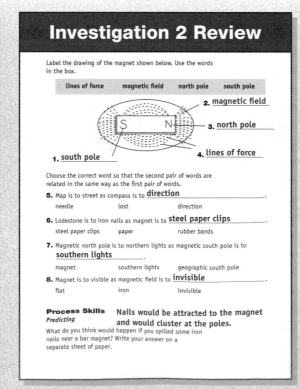

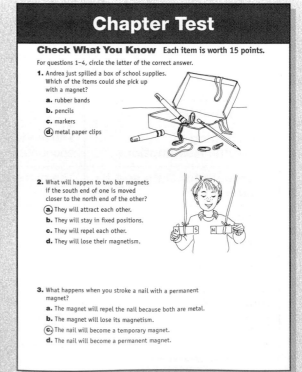

Investigation 1 Review	Investigation 2 Review	Chapter Test
Ongoing Assessment, TRB p. 117	Ongoing Assessment, TRB p. 118	Ongoing Assessment, TRB p. 119

Chapter Test

Problem Solving Each item is worth 15 points.

4. The Air Quality Act set clean-air standards in the United States. Which of the following do you think will best meet the standards of the act?
   a. railroad trains
   b. power plants burning fossil fuels.
   (c.) maglev trains
   d. gasoline-powered cars

5. Put an X on the pole that the needle of a compass will point to. On the compass face, draw a compass needle pointing to that pole.

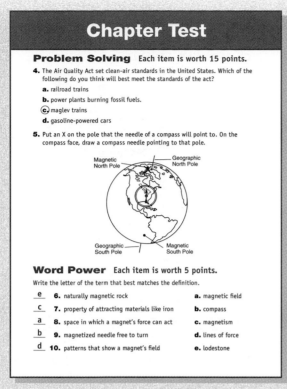

Word Power Each item is worth 5 points.
Write the letter of the term that best matches the definition.

  _e_   **6.** naturally magnetic rock   **a.** magnetic field

  _c_   **7.** property of attracting materials like iron   **b.** compass

  _a_   **8.** space in which a magnet's force can act   **c.** magnetism

  _b_   **9.** magnetized needle free to turn   **d.** lines of force

  _d_   **10.** patterns that show a magnet's field   **e.** lodestone

Ongoing Assessment, TRB p. 120

Pressed for Time Test

Check What You Know Each item is worth 10 points.
For questions 1–5, circle the letter of the correct answer.

  1. The north and south poles of two magnets _____ each other.
    a. have no reaction to   **c.** move away from
    b. repel   **(d.)** attract

  2. A horseshoe magnet has _____.
    (a.) a north pole and a south pole   **c.** a battery on each end
    b. two north poles   **d.** two south poles

  3. If you placed the south pole of one bar magnet near the south pole of another bar magnet, the two magnets would _____ each other.
    a. discharge   **b.** attract   **c.** cancel   **(d.)** repel

  4. The material best attracted by a magnet is _____.
    a. wood   **(b.)** iron   **c.** silver   **d.** glass

  5. A magnetized iron nail is called a(n) _____ magnet.
    a. permanent   **b.** industrial   **(c.)** temporary   **d.** horseshoe

Word Power Each item is worth 10 points.
Use the words in the box to answer each riddle.

north pole	lines of force	magnetism
temporary magnet	permanent magnet	

  6. I am a property that attracts iron and steel. What am I? __magnetism__

  7. I keep my magnetism for a long time. What am I? __permanent magnet__

  8. I am drawn to the south pole of another magnet. What am I? __north pole__

  9. I am a group of lines formed by iron filings sprinkled on paper covering a magnet. What am I? __lines of force__

  10. I will attract iron now but not for long. What am I? __temporary magnet__

Ongoing Assessment, TRB p. 121

Chapter 2
Assessment Options

Investigation 1 Review

Circle the word or words that best complete each sentence.
1. Unlike charges (repel, (attract)) each other.
2. Like charges ((repel) attract) each other.
3. A negatively charged balloon can stick to a wall after the (positive, (negative)) charges of the wall are pushed away.
4. When negative charges jump from a cloud to the ground, ((lightning,) rain) occurs.
5. When you walk across a rug, (positive, (negative)) charges can move from the rug to your shoes.
6. Use the phrases in the box to complete the diagram below.

negative charges move to it	becomes negatively charged
neutral before being rubbed by object	negative charges move from it
becomes positively charged	

Balloon rubbed with wool — negative charges move to it; becomes negatively charged

neutral before being rubbed by object

Balloon rubbed with plastic — negative charges move from it; becomes positively charged

Process Skills Possible answers include: Stay away from tall
Communicating trees during a storm; if in a lake or another
List three ways you can practice lightning safety. Write your body of water,
answers on a separate sheet of paper. get out when a
storm is approaching; take shelter in a building or an enclosed
car; use lightning rods on a home.

Ongoing Assessment, TRB p. 122

Investigation 2 Review

Circle the word or words that best complete each sentence.
1. Electric charges must (remain still, (flow)) to be useful.
2. An electric current is a stream of ((negative) positive) charges.
3. Charges move through a circuit that is ((closed,) open).
4. Electricity passes easily through (insulators, (conductors)).
5. Electricity powers a (faucet, (flashlight)).

6. Read the steps that describe the movement of electric charges in a closed circuit. The steps are not in the right order. Number them in the correct order.
  _4_ Charges move through the light bulb.
  _5_ Charges move through the wire leading back to the dry cell.
  _1_ Charges leave the dry cell.
  _2_ Charges move through the switch.
  _3_ Charges move from the switch to the light bulb.

Process Skills
Predicting
What will happen to a buzzer connected to an open circuit? Explain your answer.

__The buzzer will not buzz, since electricity won't flow through__
__the circuit.__

Ongoing Assessment, TRB p. 123

Investigation 3 Review

Write the letter of the term that best matches the definition.

_d_ **1.** part of a light bulb that glows   **a.** parallel

_f_ **2.** bulb filled with mercury gas   **b.** fuse

_g_ **3.** bulb that produces two forms of energy   **c.** series

_c_ **4.** circuit connected in a single path   **d.** filament

_a_ **5.** circuit that has more than one path   **e.** circuit breaker

_e_ **6.** switch that opens a circuit by shutting off   **f.** fluorescent

_b_ **7.** device that opens a circuit by melting   **g.** incandescent

Each group of terms below contains one term that does not belong with the others. Cross out the term that doesn't belong.

8. circuit breaker   ~~series~~   fuse

9. ~~carbon~~   parallel   series

10. filament   ~~mercury~~   incandescent

11. fluorescent   ultraviolet   ~~tungsten~~

12. lamps   ~~fuse~~   flashlight

Process Skills
Inferring

Why might the electricity go off in the kitchen of a house if a number of kitchen appliances are running at the same time?

The circuit might be overloaded, causing a circuit breaker or fuse to open the circuit.

Ongoing Assessment, TRB p. 124

Chapter Test

Check What You Know   Each item is worth 15 points.

For questions 1–4, circle the letter of the correct answer.

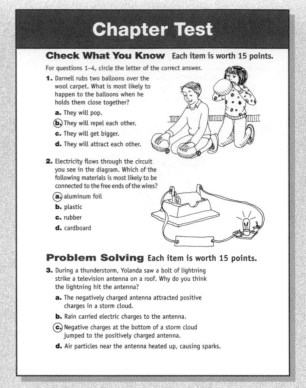

1. Darnell rubs two balloons over the wool carpet. What is most likely to happen to the balloons when he holds them close together?
- **a.** They will pop.
- **(b.)** They will repel each other.
- **c.** They will get bigger.
- **d.** They will attract each other.

2. Electricity flows through the circuit you see in the diagram. Which of the following materials is most likely to be connected to the free ends of the wires?
- **(a.)** aluminum foil
- **b.** plastic
- **c.** rubber
- **d.** cardboard

Problem Solving   Each item is worth 15 points.

3. During a thunderstorm, Yolanda saw a bolt of lightning strike a television antenna on a roof. Why do you think the lightning hit the antenna?
- **a.** The negatively charged antenna attracted positive charges in a storm cloud.
- **b.** Rain carried electric charges to the antenna.
- **(c.)** Negative charges at the bottom of a storm cloud jumped to the positively charged antenna.
- **d.** Air particles near the antenna heated up, causing sparks.

Ongoing Assessment, TRB p. 125

Chapter Test

4. Mark created a circuit for a science fair. He wanted to be able to open and close the circuit easily without connecting and disconnecting the wires. What device best suited his needs?
- **a.** a fuse   **b.** a battery   **c.** a light bulb   **(d.)** a switch

5. What kind of circuit, series or parallel, is best for a set of holiday lights? Why?

A parallel circuit is best. If one light goes out, the others will stay lit, since current has more than one path to follow.

Word Power   Each item is worth 5 points.

Use the words in the box to answer each riddle.

electric circuit	fuse	insulator
electric discharge		conductor

6. I am a friend of electricity and allow it to run through me easily. What am I?   conductor

7. I am the path along which electricity travels. What am I?   electric circuit

8. I am the crackle you hear when you touch a doorknob after rubbing your feet across a carpet. What am I?   electric discharge

9. I try to keep electricity from getting to you. What am I?   insulator

10. I keep homes safe by opening overloaded circuits. What am I?   fuse

Ongoing Assessment, TRB p. 126

Pressed for Time Test

Check What You Know   Each item is worth 10 points.

For questions 1–5, circle the letter of the correct answer.

1. A switch that opens a circuit by turning itself off is a _____.
- **(a.)** circuit breaker   **b.** motor   **c.** electromagnet   **d.** insulator

2. A circuit that has more than one path for electricity to follow is a _____ circuit.
- **a.** series   **b.** static   **c.** broken   **(d.)** parallel

3. Copper is used in wiring because it is an excellent _____ of electricity.
- **a.** circuit breaker   **(b.)** conductor   **c.** insulator   **d.** fuse

4. When a switch is turned on, you close a circuit so that it is _____.
- **a.** incomplete   **b.** inactive   **(c.)** complete   **d.** broken

5. The only charges that can move from one object to another are _____ charges.
- **a.** electric   **b.** neutral   **c.** positive   **(d.)** negative

Word Power   Each item is worth 10 points.

Use the words in the box to answer each riddle.

fuse	conductor	insulator
electric circuit		electric discharge

6. I allow electricity to run through me easily. What am I?   conductor

7. I am the path along which electricity travels. What am I?   electric circuit

8. I am the crackle you hear when you touch a doorknob after rubbing your feet across a carpet. What am I?   electric discharge

9. I try to keep electricity from getting to you. What am I?   insulator

10. I open overloaded circuits by melting. What am I?   fuse

Ongoing Assessment, TRB p. 127

Chapter 3
Assessment Options

Investigation 1 Review

Circle the word or words that best complete each sentence.

1. A device that uses a wire coil and a magnet to produce electricity is a (generator, battery).

2. In an electric cell, energy stored in (magnets, chemicals) changes to electrical energy.

3. The force that pushes electricity along wires is (charge, voltage).

4. A (transformer, generator) changes the voltage of a current.

5. Solar cells change (chemical energy, sunlight) to electrical energy.

6. Study the picture of an electricity experiment. Write O for each sentence that shows an observation. Write I for each sentence that shows an inference.

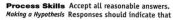

__I__ No current is flowing in pictures A and C.

__O__ The magnet is moving inside the cardboard tube in picture B.

__I__ A current is flowing through the wire in picture B.

__I__ The cause of the needle's movement in picture B is an electric current.

__O__ In picture C the magnet stops moving and so does the needle.

Process Skills Accept all reasonable answers.
Making a Hypothesis Responses should indicate that

If you were going on a remote camping trip, which kind of items would you pack in your suitcase—items powered by electrical energy that comes from chemical energy or items that plug into a circuit? Why? Provide examples to illustrate your answer. Write your answer on a separate sheet of paper.

items powered by chemical energy (batteries) are preferable for camping because electrical outlets might not be available.

Ongoing Assessment, TRB p. 128

Investigation 2 Review

Use the words in the box to complete each sentence.

electric	overloaded	electromagnet
	batteries	fuses

1. Electric cars do not pollute the air because they run on ___batteries___.

2. Household appliances, such as refrigerators and vacuum cleaners, have ___electric___ motors.

3. When a coil of wire is wrapped around a nail and attached to a dry cell, the nail can become a(n) ___electromagnet___.

4. A(n) ___overloaded___ circuit is always a safety hazard because wires can become very hot, which could cause a fire.

5. ___Fuses___ open circuits when wires get too hot.

6. Describe an electromagnet.

An electromagnet is a magnet made when an electric current passes through a wire coiled around an iron core. The magnetic force of an electromagnet can be strong enough to lift heavy objects that contain iron. Its magnetism can be turned on and off.

Process Skills
Communicating
What kinds of objects in your home or school contain electromagnets? Write your answer on a separate sheet of paper.

Answers might include loudspeakers, telephones, VCRs, tape decks, and doorbells.

Ongoing Assessment, TRB p. 129

Chapter Test

Check What You Know Each item is worth 15 points.

1. What will you have to do to close the circuit below? Show your answer on the drawing.

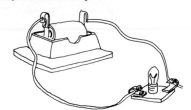

For questions 2–5, circle the letter of the correct answer.

2. Before Myra plugged in the cord of her study lamp, she noticed that the insulation on the cord was worn out. What should she do?

a. Plug in the cord, since she'll only be using the lamp for a short time.

b. Not plug in the cord until it's repaired, or buy a new lamp.

c. Be sure she holds the plug when pulling it from the outlet.

d. Plug the cord into an outlet with a number of other cords plugged into it.

Problem Solving Each item is worth 15 points.

3. Which of the following comparisons can you use to best explain voltage?

a. fire in a fireplace
b. a compass needle
c. lemon juice in a glass
d. water in a garden hose

Ongoing Assessment, TRB p. 130

Chapter Test

4. Juanita is a volunteer at a recycling center. Her job is to separate steel cans from aluminum cans. What device might make her job easier?

a. generator
b. current detector
c. electromagnet
d. transformer

5. How is an electric current produced in a battery?

a. Chemical energy changes into electrical energy.

b. Energy of motion changes into electrical energy.

c. Electrical energy changes into chemical energy.

d. Chemical energy changes into energy of motion.

Word Power Each item is worth 5 points.

Use the words in the box to complete each sentence.

generators	electric cells	solar cells
electromagnets		voltage

6. ___Generators___ produce most of the electricity that you use in your home and school.

7. Electricity sets up a magnetic field around ___electromagnets___.

8. The force that pushes electricity along wires is ___voltage___.

9. ___Solar cells___ change the Sun's energy into electrical energy.

10. A battery is made up of two or more ___electric cells___.

Ongoing Assessment, TRB p. 131

Pressed for Time Test

Check What You Know   Each item is worth 10 points.

For questions 1–5, circle the letter of the correct answer.

1. Household appliances, such as refrigerators and vacuum cleaners, usually have _____ motors.

   a. natural gas   b. solar   **c.** electric   d. gasoline

2. When a coil of wire is wrapped around a nail and attached to a dry cell, the nail can become a(n) _____.

   a. circuit breaker   b. fuse   **c.** electromagnet   d. wet cell

3. A(n) _____ circuit is always a safety hazard because wires can become very hot, which could cause a fire.

   a. overloaded   b. parallel   c. incomplete   d. broken

4. Most of the electricity used in your home and school is produced by a(n) _____.

   a. electric cell   b. magnetic field   **c.** generator   d. insulator

5. The device that opens circuits when wires get too hot is a(n) _____ .

   a. discharge   b. insulator   c. volt   **d.** fuse

Word Power   Each item is worth 10 points.

Use the words in the box to complete each sentence.

> conduct   electric cell   circuit breaker
> generator   electromagnet

A(n) __generator__ is a device that uses a wire coil and a magnet to convert energy of motion into electrical energy. An individual part of a battery is called a(n) __electric cell__ . A magnet made from wire wrapped around iron is a(n) __electromagnet__ . A circuit that has too much electricity running through it can cause a __circuit breaker__ to trip, or switch off. You should always keep an electric hair dryer away from the sink because water can __conduct__ electricity.

Ongoing Assessment, TRB p. 132

Unit Test

Check What You Know   Each item is worth 6 points.

1. Compare the two pictures of the magnetic field of a bar magnet and that of Earth. How are the fields alike?

   __Both pictures show the__
   __lines of force in the__
   __magnetic fields. Both__
   __the magnet and Earth__
   __have magnetic poles.__

2. Charged particles are forming in the storm cloud. Put a + and a − on the appropriate parts of the cloud and a + or a − on the ground where the lightning strikes.

3. Put an X on the nail that will pick up the paper clips.

4. Monica wants to make a compass. How might she construct one with the following materials: magnet, cork, straightened paper clip, plastic tub, and water? Why would it work?

   Magnetize the paper clip with __magnet and insert the clip into the center of the cork.__
   __Float the cork in a tub half full of water. It would work__
   __because the magnetized clip is like a compass needle.__

Ongoing Assessment, TRB p. 137

Unit Test

5. How are incandescent and fluorescent bulbs different?

   a. Incandescent bulbs produce light when a thin wire coil glows, and fluorescent bulbs produce light when mercury gas glows.

   b. Incandescent bulbs change light into electrical energy, and fluorescent bulbs produce a great deal of heat.

   c. Incandescent bulbs produce ultraviolet rays, and fluorescent bulbs produce light without using electricity.

   d. Incandescent bulbs change chemical energy into light, and fluorescent bulbs change heat into electrical energy.

6. When does a compass serve as a current detector?

   a. when it creates a current   c. when it interrupts the current
   b. when it detects a change in magnetism   d. when it feels the heat of the current

7. Look at the diagram. What is happening inside this dry cell?

   a. Chemical energy is changing into energy of motion.

   b. Electrical energy is changing into chemical energy.

   c. Chemical energy is changing into electrical energy.

   d. Energy of motion is changing into electrical energy.

8. The diagram shows two different kinds of electric circuits. Which of the following is true?

   a. Circuits A and B are series circuits.

   b. Circuit A is a parallel circuit, and circuit B is a series circuit.

   c. Circuits A and B are parallel circuits.

   d. Circuit A is a series circuit, and circuit B is a parallel circuit.

Ongoing Assessment, TRB p. 138

Unit Test

9. The chart shows the results of an experiment. What conclusion might you reach after studying the data?

Material	Electricity Flows Through Easily	Electricity Doesn't Flow Through Easily
Plastic		X
Aluminum Foil	X	
Cardboard		X
Copper Wire	X	

   a. Metals, plastic, and paper products can be used as either insulators or conductors.   **c.** Metals are good conductors.

   b. Metals are good insulators.   d. Plastic and paper products are good conductors.

Problem Solving   Each item is worth 6 points.

10. Keith combed his hair with two different combs made of the same material. What might happen to the combs if he put them close together right after using them?

    a. Nothing would happen.   c. The combs would break.

    b. The combs would attract each other.   **d.** The combs would repel each other.

11. Lee made a paper boat for her brother. She attached a steel screw to the bottom and floated the boat in a plastic pan half-filled with water. Underneath the pan she held a horseshoe magnet and was able to make the boat sail all around the pan. Why did the boat move?

    a. The water was attracted to the magnet.

    b. The plastic pan served as an insulator.

    c. The steel screw was attracted to the magnet.

    d. The boat was repelled by the magnet.

Ongoing Assessment, TRB p. 139

Unit Test

12. In which of the following activities do you use an electromagnet?

(a.) ringing a doorbell   c. turning on a light bulb

b. switching on a flashlight   d. turning on a circuit breaker

13. How are a solar cell and a generator alike?

a. They both use the Sun's energy.   c. They both use the energy of motion.

(b.) They both produce electricity.   d. They both use chemical energy.

14. What is an advantage and a disadvantage of electric cars?

a. They cost little to run but pollute the air.

b. They can travel long distances but only go 10 miles per hour.

c. They cost a lot to run but need a constant supply of new batteries.

(d.) They don't pollute the air but cost a lot to run.

15. Don is making a list of safety rules for his science club. What are two important items he should include on his list?

Possible answers are: Don't use an appliance with a torn cord; don't stick fingers into electrical outlets.

Word Power Each item is worth 2 points.

Use the words in the box to answer each question.

compass	conductor	generator	voltage	switch

16. What is the force that pushes electricity along wires? voltage

17. What type of material allows electricity to flow through it? conductor

18. What device opens or closes a circuit? switch

19. What do you call a magnetized needle that can freely turn? compass

20. What is a device that uses a wire coil and a magnet to produce electricity? generator

Ongoing Assessment, TRB p. 140

Pressed for Time Test

Check What You Know Each item is worth 5 points.

For questions 1–6, circle the letter of the correct answer.

1. A magnetic field _____ .

(a.) spreads out in all directions   c. moves in a straight line

b. is only at the north pole   d. is only at the south pole

2. Shaking hands on a carpet can give you a "shock" when a(n) _____ takes place.

a. incomplete circuit   c. insulation

(b.) electric discharge   d. positive charge

3. One device that uses an electromagnet is a _____ .

a. flashlight   b. compass   c. light bulb   (d.) doorbell

4. Lines of force are _____ at a magnet's poles.

a. weak   (b.) heaviest   c. neutral   d. faint

5. Rubbing a balloon with wool gives a _____ charge to the balloon.

a. positive   b. neutral   (c.) negative   d. material

6. The form of energy that comes from charged particles is called _____ energy.

a. discharge   (c.) electrical

b. static   d. solar

For questions 7–12, fill in the blank with the correct word or phrase.

7. A magnet is an object that attracts iron.

8. A temporary magnet does not keep its magnetism for very long.

9. The south pole of one magnet attracts the north pole of another magnet.

10. In a clothes dryer, a shirt with a negative charge will cling to a sock with a positive charge.

11. At Hoover Dam, water provides energy to turn large generators.

12. The two basic types of electric cells are wet cells and dry cells.

Ongoing Assessment, TRB p. 141

Pressed for Time Test

Word Power Each item is worth 5 points.

For questions 13–18, write the letter of the term that best matches the definition.

b **13.** the space in which the force of a magnet can act

f **14.** the end of a magnet that seeks north

d **15.** safety device that opens a circuit by melting

c **16.** buildup of electric charges on objects

a **17.** circuit that has only one path for electricity to follow

e **18.** machine that can produce an electric current strong enough to provide power to your entire neighborhood

a. series circuit

b. magnetic field

c. static electricity

d. fuse

e. generator

f. north pole

Problem Solving Each item is worth 5 points.

19. You should not store a videocassette tape on top of your television because this could damage the tape. Can you infer why this would harm a videotape?

The magnet inside a TV can damage the quality of the videotape. The information is stored magnetically, and it can be accidentally erased.

20. Why are most electrical cords coated in rubber? Explain your answer.

Rubber is a good insulator, so it is used to protect the user from being harmed by the electric current running through the cord. Rubber will not conduct electricity.

Ongoing Assessment, TRB p. 142

Additional Unit Support Material

Science Notebook Masters
See *Science Notebook*, TRB pp. 25–93.

Support Masters for Unit Project
See Teacher Resource Book pp. 17–21.

Letters and Activities to send home
See Teacher Resource Book pp. 3–7.

Support Masters for vocabulary development
See Reading Support Book.

Reading Transparencies for concept development
See Reading Support Transparencies.

Chapter and Unit Tests in Standardized Test Format
See *Standardized Test Practice*, TRB pp. 153–175.

An Inventor's Fair

Students construct and display their inventions that use magnetism and electricity.

Getting Ready

 Groups of 3 or 4 students

Have each group brainstorm ideas for games, puzzles, and machines they can create using magnets and electrical components. Each group chooses one invention to build. For activities in which groups work independently, each group should have an opportunity to compare its efforts with those of other groups.

Materials

For Research

- Popular science magazines
- Books on magnetism and electricity

For Models and Presentations

- Basic materials: Magnets, dry cells, insulated copper wire, flashlight bulbs, paper clips, brass fasteners, wooden boards, stiff cardboard, construction paper, modeling clay, string, and general hardware, such as nails, hammers, screws, and screwdrivers
- Additional materials (available from science supply houses): Solar cells, small motors, and test leads

Other Materials

- Unit Project Masters 1–5, TRB pp. 17–21
- *Science Notebook,* TRB pp. 33, 55, 73

Plan Ahead

Provide each group with a place in which to keep materials and inventions. Before students start to build their inventions, review their designs and plans. Have students tell you what materials they will need and demonstrate that they have carefully planned steps and coordinated their roles.

Building the Project

Through Project Links

 Chapter 1, p. D9 In brainstorming an idea for a magic trick, make sure that students recognize the potential uses of the attraction and repulsion of magnetic poles, and how the magnetic force operates through certain materials. Students may wish to use *Science Notebook,* TRB, p. 33

Assessing Student Progress: Have students display and explain drawings or models of their tricks.

 Chapter 2, p. D39 At first a quiz board game might have just one question and answer. Students may then build more elaborate quiz boards, using *Science Notebook,* TRB, p. 55 if they wish.

Assessing Student Progress: Evaluate each group's cooperative effort in building the board game and writing questions and answers. Determine if each member participates.

LINK 3
Chapter 3, p. D67 Students may work in two groups, each having one or two solar cells. Cells should be charged in direct sunlight or under a 60-watt lamp. Then have students experiment with different designs for their inventions. Students may also wish to use *Science Notebook*, TRB, p. 73.

Assessing Student Progress: Have each group explain how its plan or finished invention works.

 # Technology Link

You can have students visit our Web site at **www.eduplace.com** to access additional content-related resources, locate agencies that can help with the Unit Projects, and link to experts. You can download Unit Project Masters and obtain a scoring rubric. Classes can also share the results of their projects on-line.

Wrapping Up the Project

An Inventor's Fair

Provide a time and place for a fair at which students display their tricks, puzzles, games, and inventions that use magnetism or electricity. In addition, students can brainstorm ideas for an invention that uses both electricity and magnetism—possibly a combination or variation of the devices already developed. Students might draw detailed designs before constructing. This will help them determine what materials and tools they may need. Monitor work as it progresses. Assure students that inventions do not always work as expected at first. Encourage them to analyze what, if anything, went wrong and to propose ways of improving their plans.

People to Contact

In Person

- Have a representative from a local electric utility visit the class and relate large-scale energy production to the work students have done in the unit.

By Mail

- **American Solar Power and Wind Energy Association,** 777 N. Capitol Street, Suite 805, Washington, DC 20002

- **Electric Power Research Institute,** 3412 Hillview Avenue, Palo Alto, CA 94304

VIDEO

BILL NYE
the Science Guy

There's no one better than scientist-comic-author-former engineer Bill Nye to show students how "Science Rules!"

Magnetism

Use this episode with Chapter 1.

Proving that science always points you in the right direction, Bill explains how the invisible magnetic force that animals and pilots use for navigation is made by minerals that are plentiful inside Earth. So plentiful, in fact, that Earth itself is a giant magnet with magnetic fields that extend out into space. Simple graphics illustrate how solar winds carry charged particles to Earth's atmosphere, where the magnetic field causes the air to glow, making the northern and southern lights visible to us on Earth. Fabulous footage of the Northern lights is included.

Video Features

Nifty Home Experiment: Floating North To demonstrate magnetic north, rub a needle over a magnet about 50 times in the same direction. Put the needle on top of a plastic film cap and put the cap in a bowl of water. Watch it turn, to point north.

Way-Cool Scientist A Magnetic Resonance Imaging (MRI) specialist explains how this giant magnet allows us to take pictures of the inside of the brain.

Consider the Following Bill explains how a magnetic field forms. When iron is magnetized, its electrons' domains are lined up, making a current of electricity. The spinning Earth and its churning iron and nickel electrons create a magnetic field that causes compasses to point north.

Check It Out! Students use a map and compass to find their way through an orienteering course.

Follow-up Questions

1. What is magnetism? (Magnetism is an invisible force that comes from minerals found in the Earth.)

2. Is the Earth a magnet? (Yes, Earth has north and south magnetic poles.)

3. What three things can stick to magnets? (Iron, nickel, and cobalt will stick to magnets.)

4. Where does magnetism come from? (Magnetism comes from moving electrons, or electricity.)

▲ Science is "way cool" with Bill Nye the Science Guy.

© Disney

Science Processor
An Interactive CD-ROM

CD-ROM

The CD-ROM investigations for this unit enable students to explore the relationship between magnetism and electricity. Students create parallel and series circuits and explore a magnet and coil.

Magnetism and Electricity

Unit Opening: Shocking Behavior!
(Beginning the Unit)

Students learn that like charges repel and opposite charges attract. They view four examples to see how objects can become charged and what happens when differences in charge occur.

Investigation 1: Attractive Power
(Enhances or replaces Chapter 1)

What are magnets and magnetic fields? Students use magnets to explore magnetic objects and fields. They observe how the magnets react when brought together. They use the Painter to draw magnetic fields and use the Materials probe to determine what magnetically attracted items have in common.

Investigation 2: Lighten Up!
(Enhances or replaces Chapter 2)

How do circuits work? Students view a completed circuit and build parallel and series circuits. Students use the Magnifier to observe the movement of electrons within a circuit. They watch a video about how electricity can be generated.

Investigation 3: Power Play
(Enhances or replaces Chapter 3)

What is the relationship between magnetism and electricity? Students click on the magnet of a simple generator to explore the relationship between magnetism and electricity. They observe how the generator works and vary the number of

coils in the generator. They record their results in a Spreadsheet and view a video about the uses of electromagnetism.

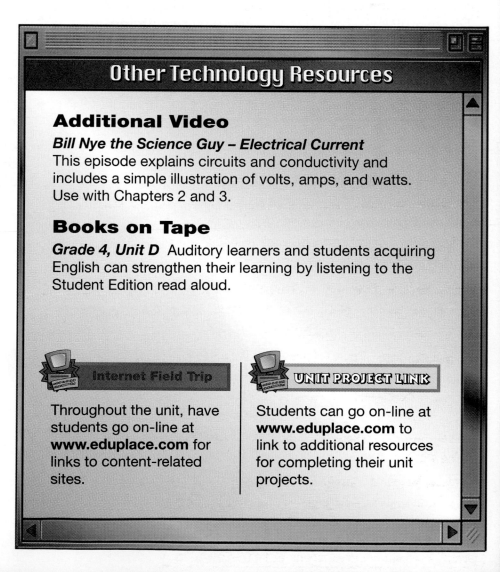

Other Technology Resources

Additional Video

Bill Nye the Science Guy – Electrical Current
This episode explains circuits and conductivity and includes a simple illustration of volts, amps, and watts. Use with Chapters 2 and 3.

Books on Tape

Grade 4, Unit D Auditory learners and students acquiring English can strengthen their learning by listening to the Student Edition read aloud.

Internet Field Trip

Throughout the unit, have students go on-line at **www.eduplace.com** for links to content-related sites.

UNIT PROJECT LINK

Students can go on-line at **www.eduplace.com** to link to additional resources for completing their unit projects.

TEACHER-TESTED ACTIVITIES

Every Activity in Houghton Mifflin Science DiscoveryWorks *was author written, teacher reviewed, and student tested.*

Developed and Tested by Authors

The Activities in Houghton Mifflin *Science DiscoveryWorks* were developed by the program authors, and have been used by them in their own classrooms. Many of the Activities have also been used in teacher-training programs sponsored by the Center for Elementary Education at Fairleigh Dickinson University. All the Activities related to astronomy and space science have been used by students at the Houston Museum of Natural Science.

Reviewed by Teachers

All lessons and chapters in Houghton Mifflin *Science DiscoveryWorks* have been reviewed by **practicing classroom teachers**. One aspect of that review was to verify that procedures are clearly written and understandable to students and that questions are appropriate and focus on the concepts being developed. Teacher reviewers provided valuable input into the Activities, including suggestions for the type of support to provide in the Teaching Guides. A list of teacher reviewers appears at the beginning of this Teaching Guide.

Field-Tested by Students

In addition to being reviewed by teachers, all Activities in Houghton Mifflin *Science DiscoveryWorks* have been field-tested by classroom teachers in their classrooms. More than 90 teachers at 9 schools across the nation worked with the program development team during these field tests. Each Activity was tested by at least two teachers in different school districts. A list of the school districts that participated in the field tests is shown below.

Science DiscoveryWorks Field-Test Sites

- Cranford Public Schools
  Cranford, NJ

- Education Center
  Dumont, NJ

- Gateway School District
  Monroeville, PA

- Dr. Charles R. Drew
  Magnet School, PS #59
  Buffalo, NY

- Mount Laurel-Hartford
  School
  Mount Laurel, NJ

- Gwinnett County Schools
  Lawrenceville, GA

- Mountain Park School
  Berkeley Heights, NJ

- Woodward School
  Saint George, UT

- Muscogee County
  School District
  Columbus, GA

MATERIALS LIST

Following is a list of materials needed for activities in this unit. Quantities are for a class of 30 students working in groups of 5. Quantities are also listed for those materials included in the Unit Kit. Additional kit options are available. Contact your sales representative for details.

Materials	Class Quantity Needed	Unit Kit Quantity	Activity Page
Consumable			
aluminum foil (strips)	1 roll	1 roll	D38
★balloons	12	1 pkg (35)	D28
★cardboard, thick	6 squares	6 squares	D36
cardboard sheets, stiff white	12		D18
cardboard strips	6		D38
cardboard tubes	6		D57
★dry cells, size D (batteries)	6	6	D36, D38, D44, D46, D56, D66
gloves, plastic	30 pairs	1 pkg (50 pairs)	D18
iron filings	6 jars	6 jars	D18
newspaper	6 sheets		D18
pencils, colored	6 sets		D44, D46
★plastic wrap	1 roll	1 roll	D28
rubber bands	6	1 pkg	D38
straws, plastic	6	1 pkg (50)	D38
★string (twine)	1 roll	1 roll	D8, D10, D28
tape, transparent	1 roll		D56
toothpicks	6	1 box (250)	D38

Materials	Class Quantity Needed	Unit Kit Quantity	Activity Page
Nonconsumable			
★bag of small objects (attracted by/not attracted by magnets)	6	6	D6
★balls, plastic-foam	6	6	D16
★battery holders	6	6	D36, D38, D44, D46, D56, D66
★bowls, small (dishes)	6	6	D16
★bulb holders (light sockets)	12	12	D36, D38, D44, D46
★cloth, wool	6 pieces	1 piece (1 ft × 2 ft)	D28
★compasses	6	6	D56
copper wires	6	1 length (4 oz)	D38
goggles	30	Safety Kit	D16, D18, D38
★light bulbs (lamps, miniature)	12	12	D36, D38, D44, D46
★magnets, bar	12	12	D6, D8, D10, D16, D18, D57
magnets, horseshoe	6	6	D18
materials, assorted	variety		D10
metersticks	6		D8, D10
★nails, iron	6	1 pkg (15)	D6, D66
★needles (with blunt ends)	6	1 pkg (7)	D16
★paper clips, small	1 box	1 box (100)	D10, D36, D38, D66
★paper fasteners, brass	12	1 pkg (100)	D36
pennies	6		D38
rulers, metric	6		D66
★tape measures, metric	6	6	D28, D56
★wire, insulated	75 ft	1 roll (25 m)	D36, D38, D44, D46, D56, D57, D66
★wire stripper	1 (teacher only)	1	D36, D38, D44, D46, D56, D57, D66

★ *Included in the Pressed for Time Kit.*

UNIT D

Magnetism and Electricity

Overview

In this unit, students will be learning about magnetism—what magnets and the magnetic force field are, what electrical energy is, and how electric circuits differ. They will also learn about some sources of electric currents and how electricity is useful.

Reading to Learn

Unit Preview Display the KWL transparency from the *Reading Support Package*.

- Ask students what they know about magnetism and electricity and record their thoughts in the **K** column.

- Ask students what they want to know about magnetism and electricity. Record their questions in the **W** column. Be sure to include the following questions:

  What are magnets?

  What is static electricity?

- You may wish to have students complete their own KWL chart using the TRB master found on page 12. Have them fill in the **L** column of the chart when they complete the unit.

Warming Up

Explain that the photo is of an aurora over Denali National Park in Alaska. Stimulate discussion with these questions:

  What do you think causes the colors of the aurora?

  What does the Earth have in common with a refrigerator magnet?

Tell students that as they work through this unit, they'll find answers to these and other questions.

Use *Science Notebook*, TRB pp. 25–26.

THINK LIKE A SCIENTIST

POLAR LIGHT SHOW

This photo shows an aurora seen from Denali National Park, in Alaska. At certain times, auroras such as this one light up the sky in brilliant displays of color over Earth's poles. What causes auroras? Scientists have learned that Earth is a giant magnet that attracts particles of matter streaming from the Sun. The displays of color result from these particles colliding with particles in the atmosphere. Although scientists know what causes auroras, they can't fully explain what causes Earth to be a magnet.

D2

Home-School Connection

The Opening Letter at the beginning of the unit introduces family members to the topics of magnetism and electricity. Distribute the Opening Letter (TRB p. 3) at the beginning of the unit.

Opening Letter

Dear Family,

How might you attach a note to your refrigerator? Why do two socks sometimes stick to each other as they come out of the dryer? How does a solar calculator work? In our science class, we will be investigating magnetism and electricity.

You can help bring science from the classroom into your home. Talk with your child about the different magnets that are in many of the appliances in your home, such as the magnet that keeps the kitchen cabinets closed. Discover ways to produce static electricity, such as rubbing an inflated balloon against your hair. Talk about how your life would be different without electricity.

CAUTION: Remember not to place magnets near electronic equipment, audio and video cassettes, or computer disks!

For this unit, we will be using the materials listed below. Can you donate any of these items? If so, we will need to receive them by _____.

- *balloons*
- *plastic wrap*
- *aluminum foil*
- *wool cloth*
- *cardboard tubes*
- *plastic bowls*
- *string*
- *plastic straws*
- *toothpicks*

Do you or any of your family members have a special interest in magnets or electricity? Can you help with activities? If so, please fill out the form below and have your child return it to class.

Thank you for your help!

- ✂

Opening Letter
Magnetism and Electricity

Your name _____ Student's name _____

Home phone _____ Work phone _____

THINK LIKE A SCIENTIST

 Questioning In this unit you'll study magnetism and electricity. You'll investigate questions such as these.

- What Are Magnetic Force Fields?
- What Is Current Electricity?

Observing, Testing, Hypothesizing In the Activity "A Magnet's Ends," you'll make observations about how magnets react with each other. You'll test a magnet and infer which end is its north pole.

Researching In the Resource "Properties of Magnets," you'll gather more information about magnets, including kinds of magnets and some uses for magnets.

Drawing Conclusions After you've completed your investigations, you'll draw conclusions about what you've learned—and get new ideas.

THINK LIKE A SCIENTIST

Before starting this unit, you may wish to have your students review scientific methods on pages S2–S9 found at the beginning of their book.

 Refer students to the two questions listed at the end of the *Questioning* section on page D3 of their book. Tell them that these questions are the titles of some of the Investigations in this unit.

 Have students select one of the questions and form a hypothesis that might answer that question.

Ask students: **What other questions would you like to ask about magnetism and electricity?** You may wish to write students' questions on the chalkboard. At the end of the unit have students determine whether or not each question has been answered.

BOOKS AND ARTICLES FOR TEACHERS

Blinkers and Buzzers: Building and Experimenting With Electricity and Magnetism by Bernie Zubrowski (Morrow, 1991). Presents experiments and projects that are designed to reveal various aspects of electricity and magnetism.

"All Aboard! For a Lesson on Magnetic Levitated Trains" by Virginia S. Moore and William J. Kaszas (*Science and Children*, February 1995). Describes activities for students that address how people have met transportation needs in the past and how maglev trains will affect people in the future.

"Science Can Be Attractive" by Michael B. Leyden (*Teaching Pre K–8*, April 1994). Discusses how magnets can be used to teach students important scientific principles, such as attraction, repulsion, and polarity.

Electricity and Magnetism by Robert Gardner (Twenty-First Century Books, 1994). Activities and experiments bring insight to the scientific properties of magnetism and electricity. Useful for classroom demonstrations.

Science in Literature

The following two books, which are featured in this unit, can be used to spark student interest in magnetism and electricity.

Magnets: Mind-boggling Experiments You Can Turn Into Science Fair Projects
by Janice VanCleave
John Wiley & Sons, 1993

Hello! Hello! A Look Inside the Telephone
by Eve and Albert Stwertka
Illustrated by Mena Dolobowsky
Julian Messner, 1991

CHAPTER 1 MAGNETISM

Subconcepts	Activities	Materials
Investigation 1 What Are Magnets? pp. D6–D15		
Magnets attract certain materials, such as iron and steel; magnets have north and south poles. *Suggested Pacing: 3 class periods* **National Science Education Standards** See page D 1c, numbers 2, 3, and 5. **Project 2061 Benchmarks** See page D 1c, numbers 1 and 2.	**Make a Magnet,** p. D6 *Science Process Skills:* observe; classify; infer; predict; collect and record data; hypothesize	**Make a Magnet** bag of small objects, magnet *, nail *, *Science Notebook,* TRB pp. 29–30
	A Magnet's Ends, p. D8 *Science Process Skills:* infer; predict; collect, record, and interpret data; identify and control variables; experiment	**A Magnet's Ends** string *, 2 bar magnets *, meterstick, 2 chairs, *Science Notebook,* TRB pp. 31–32
	Pulling Through, p. D10 *Science Process Skills:* observe; classify; infer; predict; collect, record, and interpret data; identify and control variables; experiment	**Pulling Through** string *, bar magnet *, meterstick, 2 chairs, paper clip *, assorted materials, *Science Notebook,* TRB pp. 34–35
Investigation 2 What Are Magnetic Force Fields? pp. D16–D24		
Magnets exert forces in magnetic fields. *Suggested Pacing: 2–3 class periods* **National Science Education Standards** See page D 1c, numbers 2, 3, and 5. **Project 2061 Benchmarks** See page D 1c, numbers 1 and 2.	**Getting Directions,** p. D16 *Science Process Skills:* observe; infer; predict; collect, record, and interpret data; experiment; make models	**Getting Directions** goggles *, bar magnet *, needle with blunt end *, plastic-foam ball *, small bowl *, water, *Science Notebook,* TRB pp. 37–38
	Picture a Magnet's Force, p. D18 *Science Process Skills:* observe, predict	**Picture a Magnet's Force** goggles *, gloves *, bar magnets *, newspaper, 2 sheets of white cardboard, iron filings in jar with sprinkler top *, horseshoe magnet *, *Science Notebook,* TRB pp. 39–40

Overview
In this chapter students will learn and investigate magnets and magnetic force.

Chapter Concept
Magnets, and the magnetic force fields around them, have observable properties.

Theme: Models
The properties of magnets result from the nature of the atoms that compose them. Models are useful in understanding magnets and magnetic fields.

Advance Preparation	Resources/ Vocabulary	Assessment
Make a Magnet Collect a variety of materials that students can test for magnetic attraction. Be sure to include many examples of both kinds of objects—those that are attracted to magnets and those that are not. Try to include unusual magnetic objects, such as a strip of recording tape that you no longer use or a Canadian nickel. **A Magnet's Ends** Use masking tape to cover the marked poles of some bar magnets so that each group can have an unknown magnet. Rename the poles X and Y. **Pulling Through** Gather materials for students to test, such as sheets of paper, fabric, plastic wrap, aluminum foil, and steel. Be sure that some of these materials are attracted to magnets and that some are not.	**Properties of Magnets** **Vocabulary:** magnet, magnetism, north pole, south pole **Maglev Trains**	**Chapter 1 Baseline Assessment:** TRB pp. 27–28 **Investigation 1 Baseline Assessment:** TG p. D6 **Investigation 1 Review:** TRB p. 117 **Think It/Write It:** p. D15; TRB p. 36 **Following Up on Baseline Assessment:** TG p. D15 **Performance:** TG p. D15
Getting Directions Gather some needles with blunt ends, plastic foam balls, and small bowls. **Picture a Magnet's Force** Gather newspaper and stiff white cardboard.	**Force Fields** **Vocabulary:** lines of force, magnetic field **Earth as a Magnet** **Vocabulary:** lodestone, compass	**Investigation 2 Baseline Assessment:** TG p. D16 **Investigation 2 Review:** TRB p. 118 **Think It/Write It:** p. D24; TRB p. 42 **Following Up on Baseline Assessment:** TG p. D24 **Portfolio:** TG p. D24 **Chapter 1 Summative Assessment** Reflect and Evaluate: p. D25 Chapter 1 Review/Test: TRB pp. 119–120 *Science Notebook,* TRB pp. 43–44

*Materials in the Equipment Kit   TG= Teaching Guide   TRB= Teacher Resource Book

Chapter Overview

Concept Preview

You may wish to use Transparency D1 to introduce some of the important concepts of the chapter. Students can add to the map as they complete each Activity and Resource. Then they can use the completed map as a study guide. See below for an example of a completed map.

Vocabulary Development

Use Vocabulary Master D1 at any point in the chapter for additional vocabulary support.

Common Misconceptions

Students may think a magnet attracts anything it touches. They will learn that a magnet attracts any object containing iron.

Introducing the Chapter

Warm-Up Activity

 Ask students to work in pairs to draw up a list of ways magnets are used and to categorize the uses. For example, electric can openers with magnetic lid holders are used at home.

Use *Science Notebook,* TRB pp. 27–28.

Discussion Starter

Initiate a discussion about students' current understanding of magnets, using the photo and text on p. D4.

- **How do magnets help doctors identify injuries in a patient's body?** The magnets help to produce computer images of parts inside the patient's body.

- **Why is an MRI machine so useful in a hospital?** With an MRI machine, a physician can determine the extent of an injury without operating on the patient.

MAGNETISM

Where do you find magnets? Perhaps your refrigerator door at home has small magnets that are holding up papers. You may have seen pictures of a giant magnet lifting tons of junked cars in the air. How do these magnets work?

PEOPLE USING SCIENCE

Radiologist The rear doors of an ambulance open. Quickly, Pat is wheeled into the hospital. There are bandages around her head and arm. The doctors need to make sure there are no serious injuries to her head and spine.

Pat is taken to the Magnetic Resonance Imaging (MRI) center. MRI is a technology that uses powerful magnets to produce pictures of the inside of the body.

Dr. Ray Cobb, a radiologist, gives Pat the MRI. A radiologist is trained to understand MRI pictures. The pictures help Dr. Cobb identify injuries to muscles and tissues. He can even find problems with blood circulation. In this chapter you'll find out about other ways that magnets help people.

D4

Concept Preview   ## Vocabulary Development

Transparency

How the Different Magnetic Poles Affect Each Other

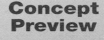

Cause → Effect

| Like poles of two magnets are moved near each other. | → | The magnets repel each other. |

| Unlike poles of two magnets are moved near each other. | → | The magnets attract each other. |

Vocabulary Master

Use the clues and the words in the box to complete the puzzle on page D35. When you have finished, read down the shaded column to answer the question.

Question How does the north pole of a magnet react to the south pole of another magnet?

| magnetic field | north pole | lodestone | compass |
| lines of force | south pole | magnetism | magnet |

Clues
1. An object that attracts or pulls on certain materials, mainly iron and steel
2. The space in which the force of a magnet can act
3. The end of a magnet that points toward the north when the magnet moves freely
4. The lines that form a pattern showing the size and shape of a magnetic force field
5. A magnet's property of attracting certain materials
6. A device containing a magnetized needle that moves freely and is used to show direction
7. The end of a magnet that points toward the south when the magnet moves freely
8. A naturally magnetic rock found at or near Earth's surface

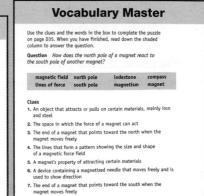

▲ **Reading Support Book**
Transparency D1

▲ **Reading Support Book**
Vocabulary Master D1

Coming Up

INVESTIGATION 1

WHAT ARE
MAGNETS?
.... D6

INVESTIGATION 2

WHAT ARE
MAGNETIC FORCE
FIELDS?
.... D16

◀ Dr. Ray Cobb studies MRI pictures to identify injuries.

D5

Chapter Road Map

INVESTIGATION 1

WHAT ARE MAGNETS?

Activities	Resources
✱ Make a Magnet	✱ Properties of Magnets
✱ A Magnet's Ends Pulling Through	Maglev Trains

INVESTIGATION 2

WHAT ARE MAGNETIC FORCE FIELDS?

Activities	Resources
✱ Getting Directions Picture a Magnet's Force	✱ Force Fields Earth as a Magnet

✱ Pressed for Time?

If you are pressed for time, focus on the Activities and Resources identified by this clock.

Home-School Connection

Distribute the Explore at Home Activity "Magnetic Mystery Tour" (Teacher Resource Book, page 4) to students after they have completed the chapter.

Technology Link

CD-ROM

Science Processor *Magnetism and Electricity*
To enhance or replace Investigations 1 and 2, use **Shocking Behavior!** and **Attractive Power**.

In **Shocking Behavior!**, students watch a video on electric charges. They experiment and discover that like charges repel and unlike charges attract.

In **Attractive Power**, students go on a scavenger hunt for magnetic objects and experiment with magnets. They click the Magnetic Fields button and "paint" field lines. Students drag objects to see which are attracted to a horseshoe magnet. They use the Materials Probe to observe properties magnets share.

Correlation to AIMS

If you use AIMS Activities, you may wish to use the activity How Will a Magnet Attract? On pages 7–12 in the *Mostly Magnets* book to further explore magnets.

Start
the Investigation

WHAT ARE MAGNETS?
pages D6–D15

Planner

Subconcept Magnets attract certain materials, such as iron and steel; magnets have north and south poles.

Objectives

- **Classify** objects as either attracted by or not attracted by a magnet.
- **Infer** the north and south poles of a magnet by the magnet's behavior.
- **Apply** principles of magnetism to real-life situations.

Pacing 3 class periods

Science Terms magnet, magnetism, north pole, south pole

Activate
Prior Knowledge

Baseline Assessment Ask: **What does a magnet do?** Make a class list of students' responses and save it for use in Following Up.

WHAT ARE MAGNETS?

Think about where you might find magnets in each room of your house. But keep in mind that many magnets are out of sight. Just what is a magnet, and what can it do? In Investigation 1 you'll find out.

Activity
Make a Magnet

Make your own magnet. Then find out what kinds of objects it pulls on, or sticks to.

MATERIALS
- bag of small objects
- bar magnet
- nail
- *Science Notebook*

SAFETY
Be careful when handling the nail.

Procedure

1. Open the bag of small objects and spread them on a table. Have each group member collect two other small objects. Include things made of many different materials.

2. In your *Science Notebook*, **make a chart** like the one shown to record your observations.

Step 3

Attracted by Magnet or Sticks to Magnet		
Object	Prediction	Actual

 See **SCIENCE and MATH TOOLBOX** page H10 if you need to review **Making a Chart to Organize Data**.

D6

Activity Make a Magnet

Preview *Students predict how magnets affect other materials and then test their predictions.*

Advance Preparation *See p. D4b.*

1. Get Ready

 GROUPS OF 3–4   **40 MINUTES**

Key Science Process Skills collect and record data, describe, predict, hypothesize, infer

 **Meeting Individual Needs**

STUDENTS ACQUIRING ENGLISH

Give students their own bags of objects. Let them classify each object as attracted to or not attracted to a magnet. Help students redesign their data chart so that the columns labeled *Prediction* and *Actual* each have subcolumns labeled *Attracted* and *Not Attracted*. Encourage them to add to these objects by testing any unusual items they might have, such as foreign coins.

KINESTHETIC

3. **Talk with your group** and together **predict** which objects will stick to a magnet. **Record** your predictions in your chart. Then move a magnet close to each object. **Record** your observations in your chart.

4. **Make a chart** like the one you made in step 2. **Predict** whether a nail will attract any of the objects. Then move a nail close to each object. **Record** your observations.

Step 5

5. Stroke the nail with the end of the magnet 30 times. *Stroke in one direction only.*

6. Repeat step 4, using the stroked nail. Make a set of predictions about the stroked nail. **Record** your predictions and, after testing the objects, **record** your observations.

Analyze and Conclude

1. **Compare** your predictions about which objects would be attracted to a magnet with your results.

2. **Compare** your predictions about the nail before you stroked it with a magnet with your results.

3. Explain your observations about the stroked nail. **Hypothesize** how stroking the nail with the magnet affects the nail.

4. What can you **infer** about the objects that were attracted by the magnet and the stroked nail?

INVESTIGATE FURTHER!

EXPERIMENT

Hold the nail that you stroked with a magnet near a pile of paper clips. If nothing happens, stroke the nail with the magnet 30 times. How many paper clips does the nail pick up?

Suppose you stroke the nail with the magnet 40 times and then 50 times. Will the nail be able to pick up more paper clips? Find out. Make a chart of your results.

D7

INVESTIGATE FURTHER!

EXPERIMENT

Up to a limit, the nail's magnetism will get stronger the more times it is stroked with a magnet. Students can experiment with the nail and magnet. Remind students to record their observations, predictions, and answers in their *Science Notebooks,* TRB, on p. 30. **Why do you think the nail's magnetism became stronger the more it was stroked?** The stroking causes more of the microscopic groups of iron atoms, or magnetic domains, to line up.

Science Processor Have students use the CD-ROM Grapher to plot the number of strokes versus the number of paper clips picked up.

2. Guide the Procedure

- For best results, the bar magnet should be as strong as possible.
- Caution students against dropping, banging, or sharply hitting the bar magnets. Doing so can affect the strength of the magnet.
- **Why is it important to stroke the nail in only one direction?** Students should conclude that it is necessary to keep from "undoing" the other strokes. (Stroking the nail with a magnet causes microscopic groups of iron atoms, called magnetic domains, to align their magnetic poles in the one direction. Reversing the direction of the strokes causes the poles to point in different directions, so the magnetic fields cancel each other out.)

Students should record their data and predictions and answer questions on *Science Notebook,* TRB pp. 29–30.

Science Processor You may wish to have students use the CD-ROM Spreadsheet to organize and display their data.

3. Assess Performance

Process Skills Checklist

- Did students **observe** and **classify** the objects in a logical and organized manner?
- Did students make reasonable **predictions**?
- Were students able to **infer** based on observations and findings? Did they infer that all the objects attracted to the magnet share a property?

Analyze and Conclude

1. Students might have expected all metal objects to be attracted to the magnet.

2. Students probably expected the nail to be non-magnetic. It might have been weakly magnetic.

3. Students might say that stroking somehow "rubbed off" magnetism on the nail and made it a magnet.

4. Students might infer that the objects that are attracted have some property in common. All objects that contain iron, such as a paper clip, thumbtack, staple, screw, safety pin, and bottle cap, are attracted to the magnet and magnetized nail. Recording tape and a Canadian nickel are also attracted to a magnet.

Activity A Magnet's Ends

Preview *Students experiment with magnets and observe how the ends, called poles, of magnets react to one another. Students should conclude that like poles repel one another and unlike poles attract one another.*

Advance Preparation *See p. D4b.*

1. Get Ready

 GROUPS OF 3–4   40 MINUTES

Key Science Process Skills predict, collect and record data, experiment, infer

Collaborative Strategy Have students draw their own arrangements for the magnets. Students should take turns testing each of their arrangements.

Materials Hints Prepare unknown magnets before class. Use masking tape or electrical tape to tape over the marking on the ends. Place new markings on the ends, marking one end *X* and the other end *Y*.

Safety Review safety precautions with students. Be sure students keep magnets away from electrical appliances, outlets, telephones, computer disks, recording tapes, magnetic identification cards, and all electronic equipment.

Activity

A Magnet's Ends

MATERIALS
• string
• 2 bar magnets
• meterstick
• 2 chairs
• *Science Notebook*

Both ends of a magnet have "pull." But are both ends of a magnet alike in every way? Find out in this activity.

Procedure

1. Tie a string to a bar magnet on which one end is marked *N* and the other is marked *S*. Tie the string to a meterstick placed between two chairs, as shown.

2. Predict what will happen if you move the end of another bar magnet marked *N* and *S* close to the hanging magnet. Think about the ways you might arrange the ends of the magnets. **Record** each arrangement and what you **predict** for each arrangement in your *Science Notebook*.

3. Make a plan with your group to test your predictions. Then **test** your plan and **record** your observations.

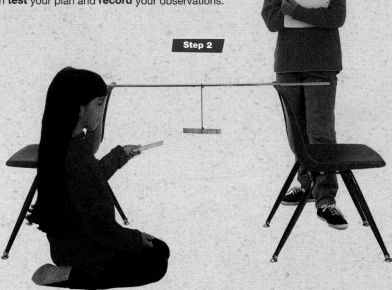

Step 2

D8

Meeting Individual Needs

EARLY FINISHERS

Students can draw diagrams showing how magnets attract and repel each other. Diagrams should have clearly labeled poles, as well as arrows that indicate how each magnet moves. Display the drawings in the classroom. Ask for a few volunteers to explain what they have drawn.

 Science Processor Have students use the CD-ROM Painter and Writer to draw and label diagrams of magnets attracting each other.

VISUAL/SPATIAL

4. Now **test** a bar magnet on which one end is marked *X* and the other end is marked *Y*. Hold one end and then the other end of this magnet near one end of the hanging magnet. **Infer** which end of the magnet you're holding is really *N* and which is really *S*. **Record** your inference and state your evidence. Remove the tape. **Record** whether your inference was correct.

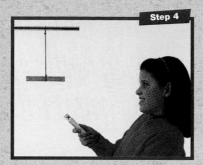

Analyze and Conclude

1. The *N* on the end of a magnet marks its north-seeking pole, or north pole. The *S* on the other end of a magnet marks its south-seeking pole, or south pole. From your observations, **conclude** which poles attract, or pull toward, each other.

2. **Conclude** which poles repel, or push away from, each other. How do you know?

UNIT PROJECT LINK

For this Unit Project you'll invent games, fun devices, and machines. You'll use magnets or electricity in all your inventions. Your first challenge is to invent a magic trick that makes use of magnets. Think about a trick that works because the force of a magnet can be "felt" through various materials. Build a model of your magic trick. Include instructions for others to follow.

TechnologyLink
For more help with your Unit Project, go to **www.eduplace.com**.

D9

UNIT PROJECT LINK

Suggest examples of tricks that students can then build on. They could move an object across a sheet of cardboard by moving a magnet underneath the cardboard. Encourage students to use not just the magnets themselves, but to affix the magnets to other objects. Students can record information in their *Science Notebooks* on TRB p. 33. Students can also use Unit Project Master 1 on TRB p. 17.

TechnologyLink
Have students visit **www.eduplace.com** to link to content-related sites and to locate agencies that can help with the Unit Project. You can also download Unit Project Masters, including a scoring rubric to assess students' progress.

---

2. Guide the Procedure

- Some students might have difficulty balancing the magnet with a single string. It may be easier to suspend the magnet in an inverted V-shaped harness using two loops of string. When suspended, the magnet should hang level.

- Remind students not to drop the magnets. Bar magnets may lose their magnetism if they are dropped. They could also break.

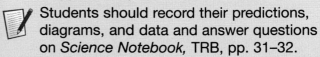 Students should record their predictions, diagrams, and data and answer questions on *Science Notebook,* TRB, pp. 31–32.

 **Science Processor** You may wish to have students use the CD-ROM Spreadsheet and Painter to organize and display their data.

3. Assess Performance

Process Skills Checklist

- Did students **conclude** that opposite poles attract? That like poles repel? Did they base their conclusions on their observations?

- Did students make **predictions** before they removed the tape? Were students able to justify instances in which their predictions were incorrect?

Analyze and Conclude

1. Opposite poles (N-S) pull toward, or attract, each other.

2. Like poles (N-N or S-S) push away from, or repel, each other. Students should cite their own observations of like poles repelling one another.

Activity Pulling Through

Preview *Students experiment to find that the magnetic force passes through both magnetic and nonmagnetic materials, as long as these are relatively thin.*

Advance Preparation *See D4b.*

1. Get Ready

 GROUPS OF 3–4

 35 MINUTES

Key Science Process Skills predict, collect and record data, experiment, infer, control and identify variables

Collaborative Strategy One student can hold the paper clip while another manipulates the sheets of materials.

Safety If using lids from canned food, be sure to tape sharp edges.

2. Guide the Procedure

- Students might need to use the V-shaped harness described in "A Magnet's Ends" to suspend the magnet.

 Students should record their predictions and answers on *Science Notebook,* TRB, pp. 34–35.

 Science Processor You might wish to have students use the CD-ROM Spreadsheet to organize and display their data.

3. Assess Performance

Process Skills Checklist
- Are students' **experiments** well thought out and results clearly **recorded**? Is there evidence that they **manipulated** the **variables**?
- Are students' **inferences** about material properties supported by observations and past experience?

Analyze and Conclude
1. Students might have predicted that a magnet's force will pass through all materials. The results of the activity showed this was not true.
2. The magnet's force can pass through different materials as long as each material is relatively thin.

Activity
Pulling Through

A magnet can have a lot of force, or pull. In this activity you'll find out more about how that force works.

MATERIALS
- string
- bar magnet
- meterstick
- 2 chairs
- paper clip
- assorted materials
- *Science Notebook*

Procedure

1. Tie a string around a bar magnet. Hang the magnet from a meterstick between two chairs.

2. Place a paper clip on the palm of your hand. Then move your hand under one end of the magnet until the magnet is just close enough to attract the paper clip.

Force of Magnet Through Materials		
Material	Prediction	Result

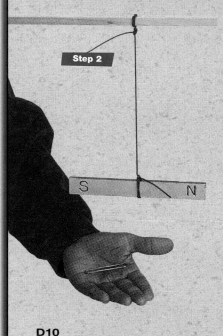

Step 2

3. **Talk with your group** and together **predict** whether the magnet can attract the paper clip through materials such as paper, aluminum foil, cloth, plastic, and steel. In your *Science Notebook,* **make a chart** like the one shown above to record your predictions and observations.

4. Plan a way to find out whether the magnet's force can act through different materials. **Test** each material, using the plan that you came up with. **Record** your observations in your chart.

Analyze and Conclude

1. **Compare** your predictions about whether the force of a magnet acts through different materials with your observations.

2. From your observations, **infer** whether the force of a magnet can pass through different materials.

D10

 Meeting Individual Needs

GIFTED AND TALENTED
After students have determined how materials affect magnetic fields, they could compose a poem that describes their results. Poems could include the idea that the thickness of a material is a factor in whether it transmits a magnetic field.

LINGUISTIC

Properties of Magnets

▲ How is a magnet being used in each picture?

What's an easy way to clean up a mixture of metal paper clips and rubber bands spilled on the floor? If you drag a magnet over the floor, the paper clips will stick to the magnet, but the rubber bands won't. Why does this happen?

The Pull of Magnets

The activity on pages D6 and D7 shows how a magnet affects some materials. A **magnet** is an object that attracts, or pulls on, certain materials, mainly iron and steel. A magnet's property of attracting these materials is called **magnetism** (mag′nə tiz əm).

Paper clips are made of steel, which contains iron. That's why you can pick them up with a magnet. Rubber bands contain no iron or other materials that a magnet attracts.

The photographs above show some uses of magnets. The part of the can opener that lifts the steel lid of the can is a magnet. Using a magnet to pick up pins keeps fingers from being stuck. A magnetic screwdriver makes it easier to hold screws in place.

The steel figures of this toy can be arranged in various ways on a magnet. ▼

D11

Integrating the Sciences

EARTH SCIENCE

What You Need samples of magnetite and hematite, reference books, a world map

What to Do Show students samples of magnetite (lodestone) and hematite. Explain that both minerals contain iron ore. Allow students to test whether or not these minerals are attracted to a magnet. Have students map where these iron ores are found worldwide.

What's the Result? Students can display their maps. **Why do you think these ores are important?** Iron is used to make cars, cookware, engines, and so on. **Where are ore deposits found?** United States: Minnesota and Pennsylvania; Europe: England, France, Germany, and Spain.

Properties of Magnets

1. Get Ready

Vocabulary

Science Terms magnet, magnetism, north pole, south pole

Support Terms attracts, property, iron

Background

- Magnets can be made of several different kinds of materials. Ceramic magnets are very affordable and come in a variety of shapes and sizes. They are used in magnetic sweepers, in tools for picking up and moving pieces of steel, and in magnetic conveyors. Many familiar household magnets are ceramic.

- One of the early manufactured magnets, Alnico magnets, is made from an alloy of aluminum, nickel, and cobalt. (An alloy is a solution of two or more metals melted and mixed together to form a new material.) Alnico magnets are permanent magnets, but they can be too expensive to use in many classrooms as well as for many industrial uses. Because less expensive ceramic magnets are also permanent, they can be a more practical choice for many applications. In many instances, the bar magnets found in classrooms are simply magnetized pieces of steel that are only temporary magnets.

Discussion Starter

- **If you could see a magnet working, what would you see?** Encourage speculation about how a magnet affects materials at a distance. Students might suggest a variety of invisible mechanisms.

- **Why do you think magnets make such interesting toys?** Use this question to evoke a list of properties. Students will probably suggest that magnets can move objects at a distance, make things float, stick things together, and so on.

2. Guide the Discussion

Choose from the following strategies to facilitate discussion.

Making Comparisons

- **What does it mean to say someone has a magnetic personality? Can someone be magnetic?** Although a personality doesn't have two poles, a magnetic personality describes a person to whom others are attracted just as a magnet attracts objects that contain iron.

- **How do the ends of a magnet differ?** Students should conclude that one end of a magnet is a south pole and will be attracted to the north pole of another magnet; the south pole will be repelled by the south pole of another magnet. The other end of the magnet is the north pole and will be attracted to the south pole of another magnet; the north pole will be repelled by the north pole of another magnet.

Making Inferences

- **Why might a magnetic screwdriver come in handy?** If you drop a screw while trying to turn it, the screw will stick to the screwdriver rather than fall to the floor.

- **What could make a freely hanging magnet point in a direction other than north?** If a strong magnet is held close to it, the hanging magnet could react to the closer magnet, rather than to the magnetic field of Earth.

Meeting Individual Needs

Inclusion Set up a learning station on the topic of magnets. Assign four facts that the students are to learn. Provide resource materials at different levels of difficulty so that each student can find information at his or her reading level.

Science in Literature

Magnets: Mind-boggling Experiments You Can Turn Into Science Fair Projects
by Janice VanCleave

Encourage small groups of students to find two ways to compare the strength of different magnets. They can present their experiments and what they discovered to the rest of the class.

Two Kinds of Magnets

Magnets made in factories, including toy magnets, are permanent magnets. A permanent magnet is not easy to make, but it keeps its magnetism for a long time. It may be made from steel that contains iron as well as other metals.

Some objects, such as iron nails, are easy to make into magnets. For example, the activity on pages D6 and D7 shows that you only have to stroke a nail with a permanent magnet to magnetize the nail. But magnets made in this way are temporary magnets. A temporary magnet is one that doesn't keep its magnetism for very long.

▲ Are the magnets on this refrigerator door likely to be temporary or permanent?

Science in Literature

MIND YOUR MAGNETS

"Magnetize a needle by allowing it to lie on a magnet for two minutes. Tie a thread to the center of the magnetized needle and suspend it inside a glass jar. Use a compass to determine which end of the needle points toward the north. Once you have identified the polarity of the needle, it can be used as a compass."

Magnets: Mind-boggling Experiments You Can Turn Into Science Fair Projects
by Janice VanCleave
John Wiley & Sons, 1993

To learn more about this and other magnet activities, read *Magnets: Mind-boggling Experiments You Can Turn Into Science Fair Projects* by Janice VanCleave.

D12

Science & Social Studies

 TESTING

What You Need audiocassettes (some iron oxide and other metal oxide), tape recorder, microphone

What to Do Explain that audiotapes use magnetic material to record sounds. The first magnetic recorder, made in 1891, used wire. In 1927, researchers developed a recorder that used a thin film coated with iron oxide. Some modern audiocassettes still use iron oxide while some use other metal oxides. Help students compare the sound quality produced by each.

What's the Result? What criteria did you use to judge sound quality? Students might observe that one type of audio tape provides clearer, less distorted sound.

▲ The south poles or north poles of two magnets repel each other.

▲ The south pole of one magnet attracts the north pole of another magnet.

North and South Poles

When a magnet is hung so that it can move freely, one end of it always points toward the north. This is the magnet's north-seeking pole, or **north pole**. If one end points north, you know what direction the other end points toward. It points south. This is the magnet's south-seeking pole, or **south pole**.

What happens if you move the north pole of one magnet near the south pole of another magnet? If both magnets are free to move, they move closer together, and the north and south poles may stick to each other.

What happens if you bring the north pole of one magnet near the north pole of another? The two magnets move farther apart. Here is a rule to remember about how magnets

behave. The unlike poles of magnets attract, or pull toward, each other. The like poles of magnets repel, or push away from, each other. In the activity on pages D8 and D9, the taped-over poles of a magnet can be determined from the way a second magnet moves. ■

Technology Link CD-ROM

INVESTIGATE FURTHER!

Use the **Science Processor CD-ROM**, *Magnetism and Electricity* (Unit Opening, Shocking Behavior!) to see how objects react when they are charged and to test objects for magnetism.

D13

Technology Link CD-ROM

INVESTIGATE FURTHER!

Students can use the **Science Processor CD-ROM** *Magnetism and Electricity*, Unit Opening Investigation, "Shocking Behavior!" to investigate more about how objects react when they are charged and to test objects for magnetism. Students view diagrams and pictures that show the movement of charges from a person's hand to a door knob. They see what happens to the negative and positive charges. Students watch a video that teaches them about shocks and lightning. Students can extend the investigation by exploring "static cling" using the Blank Page template, the Writer, and the Painter tools.

Connecting to the Activities

- *Make a Magnet, p. D6 and A Magnet's Ends, p. D8*
- **What materials did you find were attracted to the magnet? What did they have in common?** Students should recognize that materials containing iron are attracted to magnets.
- **Why do you think a permanent magnet is more useful than a temporary magnet?** Guide students to conclude that although it is easy to make temporary magnets, the magnet would eventually lose its magnetism. The temporary magnet would need to be magnetized over and over again.
- **How do like poles of a magnet behave when brought near each other?** They repel each other.
- **How do unlike poles behave when brought near each other?** They attract each other.

Meeting Individual Needs

For Extra Help Use a game as a model to reinforce the concept that opposite poles attract each other. Have the class form two teams. Each student should affix a large piece of tape to the back of each hand, one labeled N and one labeled S; it doesn't matter which is left or right. Label the ends of a baton N and S. Arrange the students in two lines and have a magnet race. Each team passes the baton down the line and back again as quickly as possible, but they must pass it only by grasping the outstretched end of the baton with the "opposite pole" hand.

3. Assess Understanding

Students can cut out strips of paper to represent bar magnets and label one end N and one end S. Then have them use at least three strips of paper to demonstrate how the "magnets" could be arranged so that each is attracted by or repelled by another magnet.

Science Processor Have students research magnetism using the Magnetism Data Pack on the CD-ROM.

Reading Focus Answer

A magnet is an object that attracts, or pulls on, materials containing iron or steel. Magnets can be used to push, pull, or pick up objects containing iron.

Maglev Trains

Reading Focus Suggest that students take notes as they read to *compare and contrast* maglev trains with other forms of transportation.

1. Get Ready

Vocabulary

Support Terms magnetic levitation, pollute

Background

• Because maglev trains are suspended in air, they eliminate the friction between wheels and rail that a regular train experiences. Therefore, maglev trains are more efficient. The trains run along a guideway fitted with electromagnetic coils. A computer determines the train's location and switches current, and hence the magnetic field, on and off in the coils. Thus, the magnetic force draws the train forward.

2. Guide the Discussion

Connecting to the Activities

• *A Magnet's Ends*, p. D8
• **How does magnetism cause a maglev train to move?** Students should conclude that the attraction of a north pole and a south pole for each other causes the train to move.

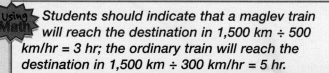

Students should indicate that a maglev train will reach the destination in 1,500 km ÷ 500 km/hr = 3 hr; the ordinary train will reach the destination in 1,500 km ÷ 300 km/hr = 5 hr.

3. Assess Understanding

Students can work in groups of three or four to draw diagrams of how a maglev train works and explain their drawings to the class.

Reading Focus Answer

A maglev train uses magnetic force to move along a rail. There is no friction between the train and the rails so it is faster and quieter than other trains. It is also clean because it runs on electricity.

Maglev Trains

Reading Focus In what ways is a maglev train different from other forms of transportation?

 Can a train fly? The maglev train does, in a way. If you visit Europe or Japan, you might ride on a maglev. It may look as if this train runs on a track, but it doesn't. The maglev train floats about 1 cm (0.4 in.) above the track!

It Flies and It's Fast

The maglev's full name tells something about how it works. *Maglev* is short for "magnetic levitation" (lev ə-tā'shən). *Levitation* means "rising into the air." The maglev uses magnetic force to rise into the air.

Ordinary trains are slowed by friction, the force caused by the wheels rubbing on the track. Because the maglev doesn't touch its track, there's no friction. This means that it can go as fast as 500 km/h (310 mph)!

Ordinary trains go "clackety-clack" along the rails. But speeding on air makes a maglev train ride very quiet, as well as smooth and superfast. What if maglev trains were everywhere? How might this affect people where you live?

 This maglev train can travel about 500 km/h. An ordinary train can travel 300 km/h. How long would it take a maglev train to reach a city 1,500 km away? An ordinary train?

D14

Integrating the Sciences

 EARTH SCIENCE

What You Need encyclopedias or other reference books

What to Do Help students recall that a maglev train depends on electricity to produce a magnetic field. Point out that electricity must be generated in some way. Ask students to find out about methods used to generate electricity, including the use of fossil fuels to power steam generators. Encourage students to find out about some of the disadvantages of using fossil fuels, including exhausting a nonrenewable resource and creating air pollution.

What's the Result? Students could draw pictures or write brief reports explaining the disadvantages of using fossil fuels.

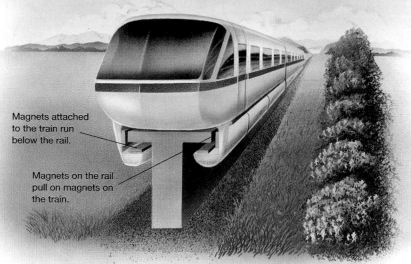

Magnets attached to the train run below the rail.

Magnets on the rail pull on magnets on the train.

▲ Maglevs are lifted into the air by magnetic forces. There are powerful magnets on both the train and the rails.

It's Clean

Most buses and cars run by burning oil or gasoline. So do most trains. When oil and gasoline burn, they pollute the air. That means those vehicles make the air dirty by giving off harmful substances.

The maglev runs on electricity. Power plants that produce electricity do burn fuels that pollute the air. But the train itself doesn't pollute the air because it doesn't burn fuels. Would you call the maglev an environmentally friendly train? Explain your answer. ■

INVESTIGATION 1 WRAP-UP

REVIEW **1.** What happens when you put the unlike poles of two magnets together?

2. What general types of materials are attracted to magnets?

CRITICAL THINKING **3.** Suppose that a rock sample from Mars is brought to Earth. Pieces of the rock can be picked up by a magnet. What metal may be present in the rock?

4. Two doughnut-shaped magnets are placed on a pencil. One of the magnets floats above the other one. What makes this happen?

D15

Close
the Investigation

INVESTIGATION WRAP-UP
REVIEW
1. When the unlike poles of two magnets are brought together, they will attract one another.

2. In general, objects made of iron and steel are attracted to magnets.

CRITICAL THINKING
3. The rock probably contains iron. *(Analyzing, Applying)*

4. The like poles of both magnets are placed next to each other, so they repel one another. The force of repulsion pushes one into the air above the other one. *(Analyzing, Synthesizing, Applying)*

CHALLENGE

Students can work in groups of three or four to design an experiment to measure the force between two magnets and how the effect of the force changes with distance. You might encourage students to use a spring scale or rubber-band scale to measure forces. Accept any reasonable experimental designs.

FOLLOWING UP

Baseline Assessment Revisit and review students' answers to the question on p. D6. Ask: **How would you change your original list? What would you add to it?**

Reteaching Use an overhead projector and two bar magnets to show students how magnets interact. You can label the magnet ends on a sheet of transparent plastic and move the magnets' poles toward each other to show how opposite and identical poles interact.

Use *Science Notebook*, TRB p. 36.

Assessment

Performance

Debate Students can debate whether a maglev train would be an asset to their community. Would good changes in the community make up for the expense of operating the train? You might guide students' preparation for the debate by asking: **How could you prove this? What would the other side say? How do you know you're right?**

Investigation Review ▶
Use Investigation Review p. 117 in the *Teacher Resource Book*.

Investigation Review

Use the words in the box to answer each question.

| repel | attract | iron |
| magnetism | temporary | permanent |

1. Which material is best attracted by a magnet? __iron__

2. How do the north and south poles of two magnets react to each other? __attract__

3. What kind of magnet is made in a factory? __permanent__

4. What is a magnet's property of attracting certain materials called? __magnetism__

5. What kind of magnet is a magnetized iron nail? __temporary__

6. How do like poles of two magnets react to each other? __repel__

Use the clues below to unscramble the letters of each word.

7. rising into the air
TALETIVINO __LEVITATION__

8. a type of magnet that doesn't keep its magnetism very long
MAPRETRYO __TEMPORARY__

9. an object that attracts materials such as iron and steel
TAMGEN __MAGNET__

10. a type of magnet that keeps its magnetism for a long time
RANMETPEN __PERMANENT__

Process Skills
Communicating Inventions should include the use of at least one magnet to pick up the fork.

Using the information in this Investigation, draw an invention on a separate sheet of paper that would pick up a steel fork.

Start
the Investigation

WHAT ARE MAGNETIC FORCE FIELDS?

pages D16–D24

Planner

Subconcept Magnets exert forces in magnetic fields.

Objectives

- **Make** and **use a model** of a compass.
- **Infer** that a magnet's field is three-dimensional.
- **Investigate** how Earth is a magnet.
- **Observe** and **predict** the effects of Earth's magnetic field.

Pacing 2–3 class periods

Science Terms lines of force, magnetic field, lodestone, compass

Activate
Prior Knowledge

Baseline Assessment Ask: **What makes one end of a compass needle point north? How do you know?** Save a list of students' responses for use in Following Up.

WHAT ARE MAGNETIC FORCE FIELDS?

You can't see, hear, or smell a magnetic force field. But bring a magnet near an iron object and you can *feel* the force. In Investigation 2 you'll explore the patterns of magnetic force fields.

Activity
Getting Directions

Earth has a magnetic force field around it. In this activity you'll make a magnet and use it to detect Earth's magnetic force field.

MATERIALS
- goggles
- bar magnet
- needle with blunt end
- plastic-foam ball
- small bowl
- water
- *Science Notebook*

SAFETY

Wear goggles during this activity. Clean up spills immediately.

Procedure

1. Magnetize a needle by stroking it 30–40 times with one end of a bar magnet. Stroke the needle in the same direction each time.

2. Stick the needle through the center of a plastic-foam ball, as shown.

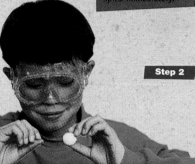

Step 2

D16

Activity Getting Directions

Preview *Students construct and test a magnetic compass and should conclude that each time the compass is turned, the needle realigns, pointing north-south.*

Advance Preparation *See p. D4b.*

1. Get Ready

 GROUPS OF 3–4   ◑ **30 MINUTES**

Key Science Process Skills make and use models, observe, record data, predict, experiment, infer

---

 Meeting Individual Needs

STUDENTS ACQUIRING ENGLISH

Have students draw a diagram showing what happens to the needle when a magnet is brought near the bowl. Students can explain to you orally what is happening or use their diagrams to indicate that they understand the concept of the activity.

Science Processor Have students use the CD-ROM Painter to draw the diagram showing the results.

VISUAL/SPATIAL

3. Half-fill a bowl with water. Carefully place the foam ball and needle on the water. **Observe** what happens. **Record** your observations in your *Science Notebook*.

4. Wait until the foam ball is still. **Talk with your group** and together **predict** what will happen if you move the bar magnet near the bowl. **Test** your prediction and **record** your observations.

5. Take away the bar magnet. Give the bowl a quarter turn. Make sure that the foam ball is free to move. Keep turning until you complete a full circle. **Record** your observations.

Step 3

Remember that a quarter turn measures 90°.

6. Then repeat steps 4 and 5 to check your results.

Analyze and Conclude

1. Find out from your teacher which direction is north. In which directions did the ends of the needle point?

2. **Compare** your prediction with your observation of what happened when you moved a bar magnet near the bowl.

3. One end of a compass always points in the direction of north. From your observations, **infer** whether or not you have made a compass. Give reasons for your inference.

D17

INVESTIGATE FURTHER!

RESEARCH

When you magnetize an object, the particles that make up the object become tiny magnets called domains. Find out more about magnetic domains at a library. One book you might read is *Magnets: Mind-boggling Experiments You Can Turn Into Science Fair Projects* by Janice VanCleave. Write a report and illustrate it with a drawing of magnetic domains.

INVESTIGATE FURTHER!

RESEARCH

Students' drawings should show the domains with magnetic poles. In the nonmagnetized material, arrows can show the fields with poles pointing in random directions. In magnetized materials, the poles of the field should align and point in the same direction. Encourage the students to record their findings and drawings in their *Science Notebooks*, TRB, p. 38.

Science Processor Have students use the CD-ROM Painter to draw the materials.

Collaborative Strategy While one group member sets up the bowl of water, another can magnetize the needle. Students can take turns moving the magnet in step 4.

Materials Hints You will need a compass to find magnetic north. Use bowls that are large enough to allow the homemade compasses to float freely.

Safety Review safety precautions with students.

2. Guide the Procedure

• If the foam ball moves away from the center of the bowl, it should be recentered.

• **Why do you think the needle pointed toward the magnet?** Students should conclude that the magnet exerted a force on the needle.

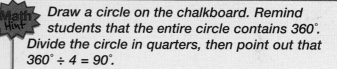
Draw a circle on the chalkboard. Remind students that the entire circle contains 360°. Divide the circle in quarters, then point out that 360° ÷ 4 = 90°.

Students should record their predictions and answer questions on *Science Notebook*, TRB, pp. 37–38.

3. Assess Performance

Process Skills Checklist

• Did students **make the model** compass correctly? Did it respond to the magnet?

• Did the students **record** their observations clearly and concisely?

• Did students **make inferences** about their compass? Were their inferences supported by observations?

Analyze and Conclude

1. The ends of the needle pointed north-south. (Note: Any differing results are likely due to large masses of iron or steel near the needle.)

2. Most students likely predicted that the magnetized needle would move in reaction to the magnet.

3. Students should infer that since their needle continued to point in a north-south direction, it meets the definition of a compass.

Activity
Picture a Magnet's Force

Preview *Students observe that iron filings trace a magnet's force field.*

Advance Preparation *See D4b.*

1. Get Ready

 GROUPS OF 2   **30 MINUTES**

Key Science Process Skills describe, predict, experiment, define operationally

Safety Warn students not to rub their eyes. Iron filings can scratch the cornea and cause eye infections. Students should wash their hands after this activity.

2. Guide the Procedure

- Make sure that students sprinkle the filings evenly.
- **What do you think caused the iron filings to line up on your cardboard?** Iron is attracted to the magnet's magnetic field along the lines of force.

 Students should record their observations, predictions, and answers on *Science Notebook*, TRB pp. 39–40.

 Science Processor Have students use the CD-ROM Painter to draw and record the patterns in steps 3, 4, and 5.

3. Assess Performance

Process Skills Checklist
- Are students' drawings of their **observations** of magnetic fields clearly labeled and accurate?
- Did students accurately **predict** the lines of force of the horseshoe magnet?

Analyze and Conclude
1. Students should observe that the iron filings are closest together at the magnet's poles.
2. The pattern of lines of force is thickest (closest together) at the poles. Therefore, the magnetic field is greatest, and the magnet's attraction is strongest, at the poles.

Activity
Picture a Magnet's Force

Even though you can't see a magnet's force, you can make a picture of it. In this activity you'll find out how.

Procedure

1. Place a bar magnet on a sheet of newspaper. Put a sheet of white cardboard on top of the magnet.

2. Hold a jar of iron filings over the cardboard. Carefully sprinkle the filings on the cardboard over the magnet.

3. Gently tap the cardboard. Look for a pattern of lines of iron filings. In your *Science Notebook*, **draw** the pattern the lines form.

4. Put a clean sheet of cardboard over a horseshoe magnet. **Talk with your group** and together **predict** the pattern that will form if you sprinkle iron filings on the cardboard. Then **make a drawing** to show your prediction.

5. **Test** your prediction. Then **draw** what you see.

6. Put the iron filings back into the jar. Repeat the experiment to check your results.

Analyze and Conclude

1. **Compare** your predictions with your observations of the patterns of the iron filings.

2. The lines made by the iron filings are a picture of **lines of force**. The space in which the lines of force form is a **magnetic field**. What do the magnetic fields you observed tell you about where the magnetic force is greatest?

D18

🧍 Meeting Individual Needs

INCLUSION
Have students manipulate two bar magnets and sense the varying attraction between them. Demonstrate how to hold the opposite poles near one another; then hold the magnet so that one pole is near the middle of the other magnet. Finally, hold identical poles near one another. Ask: **How does the force pulling the magnets vary from one part of the magnet to another?** The magnets' force is strongest near the ends.

KINESTHETIC

Force Fields

Reading Focus What is a magnetic field, and what evidence shows it exists?

◄ A magnet is strongest at its poles.

What happens if you dip a bar magnet into a pile of paper clips and then hold the magnet up? Look at the picture. A lot of clips stick to the magnet. Notice where the clips stick—at the magnet's two poles. Why does this happen?

Lines of Force

The drawings made in the activity on page D18 show force fields of bar and horseshoe magnets. When iron filings are sprinkled on cardboard over a magnet, the iron filings form a pattern.

The pattern of filings shows how the force field spreads between the poles of the magnet and around it. The filings are thickest and closest together where the force is strongest.

These lines formed by the iron filings are called **lines of force**. The picture below shows a bar magnet that was sprinkled with iron filings. Actually, it's the same magnet that was used with paper clips in the picture above. Notice how the lines of force are heaviest at the poles, where the magnet also picked up the paper clips.

Pattern formed by lines of force of a bar magnet ►

D19

Science, Technology & Society

RESEARCH

What You Need drawing paper, reference books

What to Do Explain to students that microphones change sound waves into electrical energy so that the sound can be stored, as on an audiocassette, or sent over long distances, as on the telephone. Many types of microphones use magnetic fields to make this change. Students can work independently to find out how magnets are used in microphones. They should draw a simple diagram of how magnets are used in one kind of microphone.

What's the Result? In what ways do people use microphones? People use microphones for collecting and storing sound and in amplifying and transporting sound—in films and videos, hearing aids, telephones, radios, and intercom systems.

Force Fields

Reading Focus Have students *preview* the resource to *predict* which section may provide information to answer the Reading Focus question. Have them then read to *confirm their predictions.*

1. Get Ready

Vocabulary
Science Terms lines of force, magnetic field
Support Term pattern

Background
- The organization of magnetic domains determines whether a substance is magnetized. A domain is a microscopic group of atoms with their magnetic poles aligned in the one direction. In nonmagnetized iron, the domains' poles face random directions. The magnetic fields cancel each other and the iron has no overall magnetic field. In magnetized iron, the fields have been rearranged by an outside magnetic field. They all point in about the same direction and the iron has an overall magnetic field.

Discussion Starter
- **If a magnet were immersed in oil or water, how do you think the magnetic field would be affected?** The magnet would attract iron or steel objects through the liquid.

2. Guide the Discussion

Choose from the following strategies to facilitate discussion.

Connecting to the Activities
- ***Pulling Through, p. D10***
- **What other evidence did you have that the magnetic field you worked with in the activity extended in all directions?** In the activity, the paper clip was attracted to the side of the magnet's pole.
- ***Picture a Magnet's Force, p. D18***
- **How are the paper clips like the iron filings in the activity?** Like the filings, the paper clips are thickest and closest together at the magnet's poles.

Making Inferences
- **What evidence is there that the same magnet was used in both pictures on p. D19?** Students should infer that the magnets are the same because the patterns of filings and paper clips are very similar.
- **If you dip two look-alike bar magnets into a jar of iron filings and one attracts many filings and the other attracts just a few, what would you infer about the magnets?** Even though the magnets look alike, the one that attracts a lot of filings is stronger than the one that attracts just a few.
- **If you test a magnet and it attracts paper clips but not filings, what might you infer from the test?** You might infer that the filings are not iron or any other magnetic material. Since the magnet attracts the paper clips, we know it is indeed a magnet.

A Magnet's Force Field
The space in which the force of a magnet can act is called a **magnetic field.** You can't see a magnetic field. But you have seen some evidence that it exists.

For example, suppose you want to use a magnet to pick up a paper clip. You know that you have to move the clip and the magnet close enough together for the magnet to attract the clip. That's because a magnet attracts only those paper clips—or other objects that contain iron—that come into its magnetic field.

You can see in the photos on pages D19 and D20 that iron filings can make pictures of the lines of force around a magnet. The photos make it seem that the magnetic field is flat. But is the magnetic field really flat?

The magnetic field actually spreads out in all directions throughout the space around the magnet.

Comparing Force Fields
You've found out about several properties of magnets.
- A magnet attracts objects made of iron.
- The force of a magnet is greatest at its poles.
- Like poles of two magnets repel each other.
- Unlike poles of two magnets attract each other.

How are the force fields of magnets related to those properties? Use the pictures on the next page to find out. As you look at each picture, read the description below it.

▲ The pattern of the iron filings around the magnet in this jar of oil shows how a magnetic field spreads out all around a magnet.

INVESTIGATE FURTHER!

EXPERIMENT
Explain to students that white vinegar is mainly water and a weak acid. Water alone will cause iron filings to rust; acid hastens the process. Students should use a spray bottle filled with vinegar. They can then spray a fine mist on the filings. Suggest they spray over and across the iron filings, rather than directly onto the filings. Remind students to wear goggles when handling either filings or vinegar. Encourage students to use circular, as well as bar or horseshoe magnets so there will be a variety of patterns to display on a bulletin board. Captions for each picture should tell what type of magnets were used and how they were arranged.

MAGNETIC FIELDS

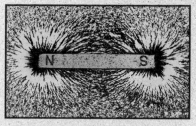

▲ This picture shows the magnetic field of a bar magnet. With your finger, trace the lines of force as they come out of the north pole, curve around the magnet, and enter the south pole.

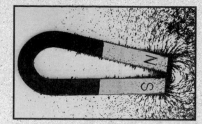

▲ This picture shows the magnetic field of a horseshoe magnet. Notice how the strongest lines are closer together than they are for the bar magnet. Infer why this is so.

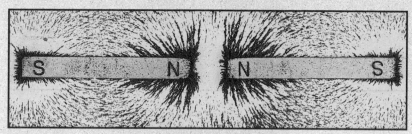

▲ The north poles of these two magnets are facing each other. What do you observe about the lines of force between the two magnets? If you hold two magnets with their north poles together like this, what will you feel?

▲ The north pole of the magnet on the left is facing the south pole of the magnet on the right. Notice that the lines of force seem to move straight from one magnet to the other. If you hold two magnets like this, what will you feel?

D21

Integrating the Sciences

LIFE SCIENCE

What You Need compass, references on migratory birds, map

What to Do Some species of migrating birds have small amounts of magnetite in their bodies, which some scientists think may aid navigation by helping the birds detect Earth's magnetic field. Students can research the migratory routes of such birds and map them. Encourage students to imagine how well they could find their way along one of these routes using a compass.

What's the Result? Ask: **Are you convinced that birds can detect Earth's magnetic field?** The presence of magnetite does not prove that migratory birds orient using magnetic fields. They may use the Sun's angle or natural landform positions.

Making Comparisons

- **How do the two patterns formed by the combinations of magnets differ?** Students should recognize that the lines of filings are thicker between closely placed opposite poles than they are between closely placed like poles.

 Meeting Individual Needs

Students Acquiring English Discuss the illustrations on pp. D20–D21. Say and write the terms *magnets, lines of force, attract, repel, north pole,* and *south pole.* Have students repeat the terms while you point them out on the illustrations.

3. Assess Understanding

Students can work in groups of three or four to invent a toy that uses one of the properties of magnetic fields they've just learned about. For example, they might suggest a painting toy that uses a small magnet to pull iron filings through paint, creating a picture or pattern.

Reading Focus Answer

The magnetic field is the area around a magnet where force can act. By using iron filings you can create a picture of a magnet's force field.

Earth as a Magnet

Reading Focus Point out that students will have to *draw conclusions* as they read this resource in order to answer the Reading Focus question.

1. Get Ready

Vocabulary
Science Terms compass, lodestone

Support Terms magnetized, North Pole, magnetic north pole

Background
• Written records referring to a "south pointer" indicate that the compass might have existed in China as early as the first century A.D. Chinese carvers fashioned spoon shapes from lodestone. When a lodestone spoon was placed on a brass plate, it rotated on its smooth, rounded bottom until the spoon's handle pointed south. Over the next several centuries, the Chinese refined this "south pointer," making it more accurate and sensitive.

Discussion Starter
• **How could you measure Earth's magnetism?** Encourage students to suggest experiments or ways of gathering data. Accept all reasonable answers.

2. Guide the Discussion

Choose from the following strategies to facilitate discussion.

Connecting to the Activities
• *Picture a Magnet's Force, p. D18*
• **If you compare the lines of force of Earth's magnetic field (p. D22) with the lines of force you saw in the iron filing experiments, which pattern is closest to Earth's?** Students should recognize that Earth's magnetic field is similar to a bar magnet's.

Earth as a Magnet

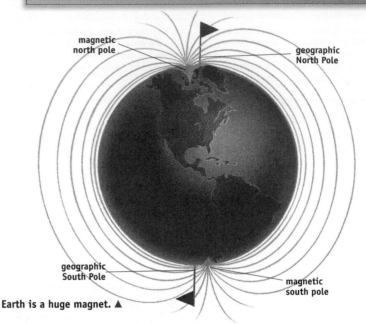

Reading Focus What makes a compass show direction on Earth?

magnetic north pole

geographic North Pole

geographic South Pole

magnetic south pole

Earth is a huge magnet. ▲

Today scientists know that Earth is a giant magnet. However, long before scientists knew anything about Earth's magnetism, they knew about lodestone (lōd'stōn).

Lodestone is a naturally magnetic rock found at or near Earth's surface. The first lodestone was discovered by a sheepherder in Turkey more than 2,000 years ago. The stone attracted iron nails in the sheepherder's shoes. Almost 1,000 years later the Greeks made a discovery. They found that when hung from a string, lodestone always lined itself up in a north-south direction. The same end of the lodestone always pointed north.

D22

Science & Social Studies

MAPPING

What You Need compass, topographic map, list of landmarks

What to Do Explain that orienteering is an outdoor sport based on finding your way to a goal across unfamiliar territory. Competitors are given a list of landmarks and compass headings to find their way. Challenge students to create an orienteering game using landmarks and compass headings from their school or community.

What's the Result? What did you find challenging about orienteering? Where might these skills be useful? Using compass headings can be difficult since it requires knowledge of angles. The skills might be useful in a wilderness.

A Stone Leads the Way

Chinese sailors found a practical use for lodestone. They floated a small piece of lodestone on some straw in a bowl of water. Since one end of the stone always pointed toward the north, the sailors always knew in which direction they were sailing.

The device used by the Chinese sailors is easy to make. In the activity on pages D16 and D17, a similar device is made with a magnetized needle and a foam ball. The device is a simple compass. A **compass** is a magnetized needle that is allowed to swing freely.

Earth's Magnetism

Since the discovery of lodestones, scientists have learned that Earth's center is made up mostly of iron. They know that the spinning of Earth on its axis has magnetized this iron, turning Earth into a giant magnet. But they can't explain how the spinning causes this.

The "Earth magnet" has poles. It is surrounded by a magnetic field with lines of force like those that can be seen in the activity on page D18. Magnets are affected by Earth's magnetic field. The north-seeking pole of a magnet is attracted to Earth's magnetic north pole. This attraction is what makes a compass work.

Why Two Sets of Poles?

As the drawing on page D22 shows, Earth has two sets of poles—geographic and magnetic. The geographic poles mark the ends of the imaginary line, or axis, around which Earth rotates.

When the first explorers set out for the North Pole, they expected their compass to lead them to the geographic North Pole. But it didn't. Their compass led the explorers to a spot more than 1,600 km (1,000 mi) from the geographic North Pole. This spot marks the location of Earth's magnetic north pole.

A piece of lodestone ▼

▲ **This ancient Chinese compass is a spoon that turns so that its handle points south.**

D23

Meeting Individual Needs

For Extra Help Some students might not readily visualize the difference between geographic north and magnetic north. Use a map or globe to point out that the geographic North Pole is where the lines of longitude meet. The magnetic north pole is the point toward which north-seeking compass needles point.

3. Assess Understanding

Students can work in groups of three or four to design a bulletin board showing Earth's magnetic field and the locations of true north and magnetic north.

Internet Field Trip

From **www.eduplace.com** students can link to a Web site about Earth's magnetism. A trip log will guide their visit to the site.

Reading Focus Answer

Earth is a giant magnet with a magnetic field. The north-seeking pole of a magnet is attracted to Earth's magnetic pole. Because a compass needle is magnetized, its north-seeking pole is attracted to the Earth's magnetic north pole.

Science Around the World

USING MAPS

What You Need map of Pacific Ocean

What to Do Explain that Polynesian sailors often navigate huge stretches of ocean without using compasses. Instead, they use the shape of waves, the color of the sky, and the stars to find their location and keep them on course. Ask students what might be the benefits of having a compass to use, and what might be the benefits of knowing how to navigate without one.

What's the Result? Students imagine they are about to sail the Pacific Ocean. They might write a brief statement of how they intend to navigate on the journey, using either navigation method alone or using both methods together.

INVESTIGATION WRAP-UP

REVIEW

1. A magnetic field is the space in which the force of a magnet can act.

2. Earth is like a magnet because it has two poles and is surrounded by a magnetic field.

CRITICAL THINKING

3. The poles of the circular magnet must be located on its faces. *(Analyzing, Evaluating)*

4. Tie the string around the nail and tape the end of the string to the underside of the jar lid at its center. Screw the lid on the jar with the nail hanging from the lid. Use a ready-made compass to determine which end of the nail points north. *(Analyzing, Evaluating, Solving Problems)*

CHALLENGE

Students could predict and draw the patterns of force for combinations of magnet shapes, such as a horseshoe magnet facing two bar magnets. After predictions are complete, challenge them to test their predictions.

FOLLOWING UP

Baseline Assessment Revisit and review the question about why compass needles point north. Ask student volunteers to draw a diagram on the board that shows the force that makes a compass needle point north.

Reteaching Display a globe. Trace lines of force from the north pole to the south pole. Point out that magnetic field lines extend on all sides of Earth and in all directions.

 Use *Science Notebook*, TRB, p. 42.

▲ **An aurora in the northern sky**

Magnetism Lights Up the Sky

At certain times of the year, people living in regions near the poles get a special treat. They get to see the northern or southern lights. During these times, the sky above the poles lights up in a display of brilliant colors. The times when these displays occur are also marked by disturbances of radio signals.

These displays, called auroras (ô rôr′əz), are produced when particles of matter from space are captured by Earth's magnetic field. Why are these displays brightest near Earth's magnetic poles? ■

Internet Field Trip
Visit **www.eduplace.com** to find out more about Earth's magnetism.

INVESTIGATION 2 WRAP-UP

REVIEW **1.** What is a magnetic field?

2. Compare Earth to a magnet.

CRITICAL THINKING **3.** When a circular magnet is dipped into a pile of paper clips, about the same number of clips sticks to the top as to the bottom. What does this tell you about the magnetic field of that magnet?

4. How could you make a compass with a magnetized nail, a string, a plastic jar with a lid, and some tape?

D24

Assessment

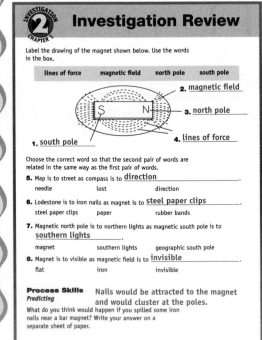

Investigation Review

Label the drawing of the magnet shown below. Use the words in the box.

| lines of force | magnetic field | north pole | south pole |

2. magnetic field
3. north pole
1. south pole
4. lines of force

Choose the correct word so that the second pair of words are related in the same way as the first pair of words.

5. Map is to street as compass is to **direction**
needle   lost   direction

6. Lodestone is to iron nails as magnet is to **steel paper clips**
steel paper clips   paper   rubber bands

7. Magnetic north pole is to northern lights as magnetic south pole is to **southern lights**
magnet   southern lights   geographic south pole

8. Magnet is to visible as magnetic field is to **invisible**
flat   iron   invisible

Process Skills Nails would be attracted to the magnet
Predicting and would cluster at the poles.
What do you think would happen if you spilled some iron nails near a bar magnet? Write your answer on a separate sheet of paper.

Portfolio

Drawing Invite students to make labeled drawings showing the magnetic fields of various shapes of magnets. Drawings should indicate the field lines and poles of each shape of magnet. They might also use their drawings to explain why magnets of certain shapes are used for a particular purpose.

◀ **Investigation Review**
Use Investigation Review p. 118 in the *Teacher Resource Book*.

REFLECT & EVALUATE

Word Power

Write the letter of the term that best completes each sentence. *Not all terms will be used.*

1. A magnet's property of attracting iron is called ___.
2. The end of a magnet that seeks north is its ___.
3. The space in which the force of a magnet can act is called a ___.
4. A magnetized needle that swings freely is a ___.
5. A naturally magnetic rock is called ___.
6. The end of a magnet that seeks south is its ___.

a. compass
b. lines of force
c. lodestone
d. magnetic field
e. magnetism
f. north pole
g. south pole

Check What You Know

Write the term in each pair that best completes each sentence.

1. Lines formed by iron filings near a magnet are (lines of force, poles).
2. The force of a magnet is greatest at its (center, poles).
3. A magnet can be used to pick up (wood, iron).
4. If the south poles of two magnets are brought near each other, the poles (attract, repel) each other.

Problem Solving

1. Suppose that you are lost in the woods. You do not have a compass, but you do have a bar magnet and some string. How can you use the magnet and string to find your way?

2. You have two magnets—one strong and one weak. How could you use paper clips to find out which magnet is stronger?

Study the photograph. Explain whether the magnetic poles that are closest together are like or unlike. In your own words, write how you know this.

D25

Assessment

Chapter Test

Check What You Know Each item is worth 15 points.

For questions 1–4, circle the letter of the correct answer.

1. Andrea just spilled a box of school supplies. Which of the items could she pick up with a magnet?
   a. rubber bands
   b. pencils
   c. markers
   (d.) metal paper clips

2. What will happen to two bar magnets if the south end of one is moved closer to the north end of the other?
   (a.) They will attract each other.
   b. They will stay in fixed positions.
   c. They will repel each other.
   d. They will lose their magnetism.

3. What happens when you stroke a nail with a permanent magnet?
   a. The magnet will repel the nail because both are metal.
   b. The magnet will lose its magnetism.
   (c.) The nail will become a temporary magnet.
   d. The nail will become a permanent magnet.

Chapter Test

Problem Solving Each item is worth 15 points.

4. The Air Quality Act set clean-air standards in the United States. Which of the following do you think will best meet the standards of the act?
   a. railroad trains
   b. power plants burning fossil fuels.
   c. maglev trains
   d. gasoline-powered cars

5. Put an X on the pole that the needle of a compass will point to. On the compass face, draw a compass needle pointing to that pole.

Magnetic North Pole
Geographic North Pole
Geographic South Pole
Magnetic South Pole

Word Power Each item is worth 5 points.

Write the letter of the term that best matches the definition.

___ 6. naturally magnetic rock
___ 7. property of attracting materials like iron
___ 8. space in which a magnet's force can act
___ 9. magnetized needle free to turn
___ 10. patterns that show a magnet's field

a. magnetic field
b. compass
c. magnetism
d. lines of force
e. lodestone

REFLECT & EVALUATE

Word Power

1. e   **2.** f   **3.** d   **4.** a   **5.** c   **6.** g

Check What You Know

1. lines of force   **2.** poles   **3.** iron   **4.** repel

Problem Solving

1. You could tie the string to the middle of the magnet and allow the magnet to hang free. The end marked N should point north.

2. You could see which magnet picks up more paper clips. The stronger magnet will pick up more clips.

The poles are alike. The space between them is clear of iron filings, so they must be repelling each other. If the poles were unlike, they would attract each other, and the space between them would be filled with iron filings that show lines of force between the magnets.

Assess Performance

Student Task

Direct students to plan an experiment to find out how the number of times a needle is stroked with a magnet affects the length of time the needle remains magnetized. Allow students to execute their plans after you have reviewed them.

Scoring Rubric

Points	What to Look For
3	Student has a clear plan that tests the relationship between the stroked needle and its magnetism.
2	Student's plan is generally logical but some aspects of data collection and variable control are either not accurate or not stated clearly.
1	The plan is unclear, illogical, and does not test the relationship in question.

◀ **Chapter Test**

Use pp. 119–120 in the *Teacher Resource Book.*

REFLECT AND EVALUATE D 25

CHAPTER 2 ELECTRICAL ENERGY

Subconcepts	Activities	Materials

Investigation 1 What Is Static Electricity? pp. D28–D35

Static electricity consists of an electric charge on the surface of an object.

Suggested Pacing: 2–3 class periods

National Science Education Standards
See page D 1c, numbers 3 and 5.

Project 2061 Benchmarks
See page D 1c, numbers 1 and 3.

Charge!, p. D28
Science Process Skills: observe, measure and use numbers, infer, predict, interpret data

---

Charge!
2 balloons *, 2 strings (30 cm each) *, metric tape measure *, wool cloth *, plastic wrap *, *Science Notebook,* TRB pp. 48–49

Investigation 2 What Is Current Electricity? pp. D36–D43

Current electricity is a flow of negative charges through a conductor in a closed circuit.

Suggested Pacing: 3–4 class periods

National Science Education Standards
See page D 1c, numbers 1, 3, and 5.

Project 2061 Benchmarks
See page D 1c, number 1.

On or Off?, p. D36
Science Process Skills: predict, identify and control variables, define operationally, hypothesize, experiment

Stop or Go?, p. D38
Science Process Skills: classify; infer; predict; collect, record, and interpret data; identify and control variables; define operationally; experiment

---

On or Off?
dry cell (size D) in holder *, light bulb in holder *, 3 insulated wires (stripped on ends) *, thick cardboard *, 2 brass paper fasteners *, paper clip *, *Science Notebook,* TRB pp. 51–52

Stop or Go?
goggles *, 3 insulated wires (stripped on ends) *, light bulb in holder *, dry cell (size D) in holder *, copper wire *, plastic straw *, penny, toothpick *, paper clip *, rubber band *, cardboard strip *, aluminum foil strip *, *Science Notebook,* TRB pp. 53–54

Investigation 3 How Do Electric Circuits Differ? pp. D44–D52

Electric circuits can be put together in series or in parallel.

Suggested Pacing: 3–4 class periods

National Science Education Standards
See page D 1c, numbers 1, 3, and 5.

Project 2061 Benchmarks
See page D 1c, number 1.

One Type of Circuit, p. D44
Science Process Skills: infer; predict; collect, record, and interpret data; define operationally

Another Type of Circuit, p. D46
Science Process Skills: infer; predict; collect, record, and interpret data; define operationally

---

One Type of Circuit
dry cell (size D) in holder *, 3 insulated wires (stripped on ends) *, 2 light bulbs in holders *, colored pencils, *Science Notebook,* TRB pp. 57–58

Another Type of Circuit
dry cell (size D) in holder *, 4 insulated wires (stripped on ends) *, 2 light bulbs in holders *, *Science Notebook,* TRB pp. 59–60

Overview
Students will learn about static electricity, current electricity, and types of electric circuits.

Chapter Concept
There are two forms of electrical energy—static and current.

Theme: Systems
In order for current to flow through an electrical system a circuit must be closed. When a circuit is open, there is a break in the pathway, which keeps current from flowing through the system.

Advance Preparation	Resources/ Vocabulary	Assessment
Charge! None	**Static Electricity** **Vocabulary:** electric charges, static electricity, electric discharge **Lightning**	**Chapter 2 Baseline Assessment:** TRB pp. 45–46 **Investigation 1 Baseline Assessment:** TG p. D28 **Investigation 1 Review:** TRB p. 122 **Think It/Write It:** p. D35; TRB p. 50 **Following Up on Baseline Assessment:** TG p. D35 **Portfolio:** TG p. D35
On or Off? Test all bulbs. Using a wire stripper or scissors, cut enough 30-cm pieces of insulated copper wire to supply 3 pieces of the wire to each group. Strip 2 cm of insulation from both ends of each piece. **Stop or Go?** Test bulbs and prepare wires as described for the activity On or Off?, or reuse the same wires.	**Electric Current** **Vocabulary:** electric current, electric circuit, switch, conductors, insulators	**Investigation 2 Baseline Assessment:** TG p. D36 **Investigation 2 Review:** TRB p. 123 **Think It/Write It:** p. D43; TRB p. 56 **Following Up on Baseline Assessment:** TG p. D43 **Performance:** TG p. D43
One Type of Circuit Test bulbs and prepare wires as described for the activity On or Off?, or reuse the same wires. **Another Type of Circuit** Test bulbs and prepare as many wires as needed, as described for the activity On or Off?	**The Light Bulb** **Vocabulary:** filament **Series and Parallel Circuits** **Vocabulary:** series circuit, parallel circuit, fuse, circuit breaker	**Investigation 3 Baseline Assessment:** TG p. D44 **Investigation 3 Review:** TRB p. 124 **Think It/Write It:** p. D52; TRB p. 62 **Following Up on Baseline Assessment:** TG p. D52 **Portfolio:** TG p. D52 **Chapter 2 Summative Assessment** Reflect and Evaluate: p. D53 Chapter 2 Review/Test: TRB pp. 125–126 *Science Notebook,* TRB pp. 63–64

*Materials in the Equipment Kit   TG= Teaching Guide   TRB= Teacher Resource Book

Chapter Overview

Concept Preview

You may wish to use Transparency D2 to introduce some of the important concepts of the chapter. Students can add to the map as they complete each Activity and Resource. Then they can use the completed map as a study guide.

Vocabulary Development

Use Vocabulary Master D2 at any point in the chapter for additional vocabulary support.

Common Misconceptions

Students may think electricity and magnetism are unrelated. In this chapter they will see that electricity and magnets have some characteristics in common.

Introducing the Chapter

Warm-Up Activity

 Direct small groups of students to list the electrical appliances their family uses often. Then discuss with the class how the tasks could be performed without electricity.

Use *Science Notebook*, TRB pp. 45–46.

Discussion Starter

Initiate a discussion about students' current understanding of electricity, using the photo and text on p. D26.

• **Why do you think David Archer calls the shapes he forms art storms?** They are formed by lightning-like arcs and are cloudy shapes.

• **How does David Archer run his electric paintbrush?** He uses household electricity.

CHAPTER
2

ELECTRICAL ENERGY

What does a comic-book artist show by drawing a zigzag line? How can you tell that a character in a cartoon is having a bright idea? Think of some other signs and symbols that stand for electrical energy in action.

. . . .

Connecting to Science
ARTS

Electric Art Artist David Archer creates pictures with an electric paintbrush. This device produces lightninglike arcs of electricity. Archer uses a wand to direct the arcs so that they hit large blobs of wet paint. The paint forms cloudy shapes on large glass plates. The artist calls these shapes art storms.

Most often, David Archer paints pictures of planets and other bodies in space as he imagines them. His work has appeared in magazines and even in the movies. You may have seen some of this artist's works on a television science-fiction show.

To run his electric paintbrush, David Archer uses household electricity. In this chapter you'll find out more about why electricity is such hot stuff!

D26

Concept Preview

Transparency

Comparing Two Kinds of Electrical Circuits

Series Circuit	Parallel Circuit

Current follows a single path

Is a kind of electric circuit

Current can follow more than one path

Current stops if one bulb is removed

Has electric current that flows in one direction

Current flows if one or more bulbs are removed

▲ Reading Support Book
Transparency D2

Vocabulary Development

Vocabulary Master

Use the words in the box to complete each sentence.

electric charges	static electricity	series circuit	filament
electric discharge	circuit breaker	parallel circuit	switch
electric current	conductors	insulators	fuse
electric circuit			

1. The loss or release of an electric charge is called a(n) **electric discharge**.

2. The units of electricity that some particles of matter carry are called **electric charges**.

3. Materials through which electricity does not move easily are called **insulators**.

4. A(n) **parallel circuit** is an electric circuit that has more than one path along which electric current can travel.

5. A continuous flow of negative charges is called a(n) **electric current**.

6. The long, thin coil of wire in an incandescent light bulb that glows when electricity passes through it is called the **filament**.

7. A(n) **switch** is a device that opens or closes a circuit.

8. A switch that opens a circuit by turning itself off is called a(n) **circuit breaker**.

9. The buildup of electric charges on the surface of an object is called **static electricity**.

10. A device in a circuit that contains a metal strip that melts when the circuit is overheated is called a(n) **fuse**.

11. Materials that allow electricity to pass through them easily are called **conductors**.

12. A path along which an electric current can move is called a(n) **electric circuit**.

13. A(n) **series circuit** is an electric circuit in which the parts are connected in a single path.

▲ Reading Support Book
Vocabulary Master D2

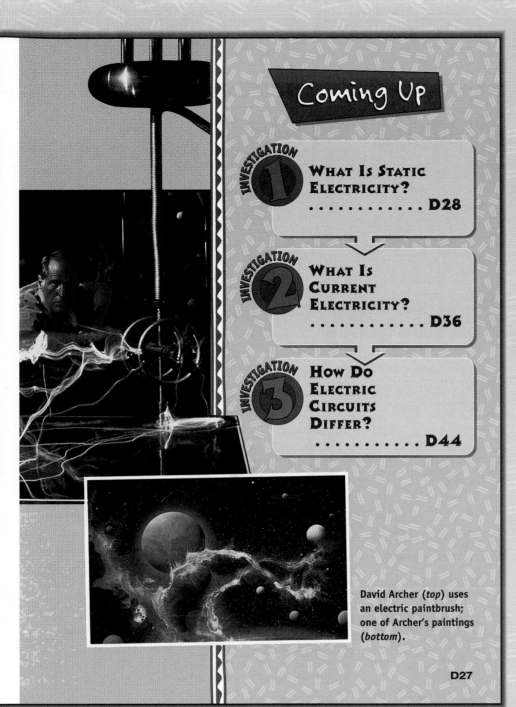

Coming Up

David Archer (*top*) uses
an electric paintbrush;
one of Archer's paintings
(*bottom*).

D27

Chapter Road Map

 INVESTIGATION 1

WHAT IS STATIC ELECTRICITY?

Activities	Resources
* Charge!	* Static Electricity Lightning

 INVESTIGATION 2

WHAT IS CURRENT ELECTRICITY?

Activities	Resources
* On or Off? Stop or Go?	* Electric Current

INVESTIGATION 3

HOW DO ELECTRIC CIRCUITS DIFFER?

Activities	Resources
* One Type of Circuit	The Light Bulb
* Another Type of Circuit	* Series and Parallel Circuits

* Pressed for Time?

If you are pressed for time, focus on the Activities and Resources identified by this clock.

Home-School Connection

Distribute the Explore at Home Activity "Flying Foil" (Teacher Resource Book, page 5) to students after they have completed the chapter.

Technology Link

CD-ROM

Science Processor *Magnetism and Electricity*
To enhance or replace Investigation 3, use **Lighten Up!**

In **Lighten Up!**, students learn that an electric circuit must have a complete path in order to work. They discover that circuits can be put together in series or in parallel by assembling examples of each and testing them to determine their characteristics.

Using a "Magnifier," students examine a section of a wire (lead) and write their observations in the Science Notebook. Students also view a video about ways that electricity can be generated.

 Correlation to
AIMS

If you use AIMS Activities, you may wish to use the activity Different Strokes on pages 9–12 in the *Electrical Connections* book to further explore static electricity.

Start
the Investigation

WHAT IS STATIC ELECTRICITY?
pages D28–D35

Planner

Subconcept Static electricity consists of an electric charge on the surface of an object.

Objectives

- **Predict** and **test** the effects of static electricity.
- **Apply** knowledge of static electricity to observations of everyday phenomena.

Pacing 2–3 class periods

Science Terms electric charges, static electricity, electric discharge

Activate Prior Knowledge

Baseline Assessment Ask students to make a small pile of paper bits, comb their hair briskly, and bring the comb over the paper. Ask: **Why do you think the comb picked up the paper?** Save class responses for use in Following Up.

WHAT IS STATIC ELECTRICITY?

Your clean hair clings to your comb. A shirt you take out of the dryer has socks stuck to it. As you pull up a blanket on a chilly night, you see sparks and feel a slight shock. In Investigation 1 you'll find out how all these events are related.

Activity
Charge!

Sometimes a balloon will stick to another balloon; other times it won't. Try this activity and see if you can figure out why.

MATERIALS
- 2 balloons
- 2 strings (30 cm each)
- metric tape measure
- wool cloth
- plastic wrap
- *Science Notebook*

Procedure

1. Have two members of your group blow up balloons. Tie each balloon tightly with a string.

2. Have two other group members hold the strings so that the balloons hang about 10 cm apart. **Observe** any movement. **Record** your observations in your *Science Notebook*.

 See **SCIENCE** and **MATH TOOLBOX** page H6 if you need to review **Using a Tape Measure or Ruler.**

Step 1

D28

Activity Charge!

Preview *Students find that balloons repel each other when rubbed with the same material and are attracted to each other when rubbed with different materials.*

1. Get Ready

 GROUPS OF 4–6   **40 MINUTES**

Key Science Process Skills observe, measure, predict, infer

Collaborative Strategy One group member might record data; another could describe what happens, while other members suspend the balloons by strings.

 ## Meeting Individual Needs

STUDENTS ACQUIRING ENGLISH

In your pre-activity discussion review the terms *repel* and *attract*. Explain that *push away* and *pull together* have the same meaning. Sketch several simple diagrams on the board and have students label them "attract" and "repel". Leave them on the board for students to reference during the activity. Encourage students to add drawings to their observations to help them describe their results.

LINGUISTIC

3. Rub each balloon with a wool cloth. **Predict** what will happen now if you repeat step 2. **Talk with your group** and **record** your prediction. Then repeat step 2.

4. Repeat step 3, but this time rub each balloon with plastic wrap instead of a wool cloth.

Step 3

5. With your group, **predict** what will happen when a balloon rubbed with wool is brought near a balloon rubbed with plastic wrap. **Test** your prediction and **record** your observations.

Analyze and Conclude

1. Rubbing a balloon with wool or plastic wrap gives the balloon an electric charge. From observing the behavior of the balloons, **infer** whether there is more than one kind of electric charge. Explain how you made your inference.

2. **Compare** your prediction about the balloons with your observations after they were rubbed with the wool cloth.

3. **Compare** your prediction about the balloons with your observations after they were rubbed with the plastic wrap.

4. Like charges repel, or push away from, each other. Unlike charges attract, or pull toward, each other. How do your results support these statements?

INVESTIGATE FURTHER!

EXPERIMENT

How does a balloon that has been charged interact with objects that have not been charged? Bring a charged balloon close to some puffed-cereal grains. Then bring another charged balloon near a wall. What can you conclude about the effect of a charged balloon on uncharged objects?

D29

INVESTIGATE FURTHER!

EXPERIMENT

A charged balloon will attract and pick up a few puffed cereal grains. Students may conclude that the charged balloon causes the grains to acquire a charge opposite to that of the balloon, but they are not likely to be able to explain how this happens without reading the Resource article that follows. Tell students to record their notes and observations on *Science Notebook*, TRB, p. 49.

Materials Hints Use round balloons. Be sure that the cloth is 100 percent wool.

Safety Review safety precautions with students. Caution students to use care when blowing up balloons.

2. Guide the Procedure

- This activity will work best on days when the humidity is low.
- **Does it matter how many times you rub the balloon with the materials? Find out.** The amount of rubbing matters but only up to a point. There is a point beyond which no additional charges can be transferred.

 Have students record their predictions and answer questions on *Science Notebook*, TRB, pp. 47–49.

 Science Processor Students can use the CD-ROM Painter to make diagrams to explain what is happening between the balloons.

3. Assess Performance

Process Skills Checklist
- Did students **predict** how the balloons would behave when rubbed with wool or plastic? Did they **predict** that the balloons would move?
- Did students **interpret** their **data** to support statements about like charges repelling and unlike charges attracting?

Analyze and Conclude
1. When both balloons were rubbed with wool or plastic wrap, they repelled each other. When one was rubbed with wool and the other with plastic wrap, they attracted each other. So there must be at least two kinds of electric charge, one produced by the wool and the other by the plastic wrap.

2. Predictions should be reasonable but need not correspond to observations. Balloons repelled each other when both were rubbed with wool cloth.

3. Balloons repelled each other when both were rubbed with plastic wrap.

4. The two balloons rubbed with wool had like charges, and they repelled each other. The two balloons rubbed with plastic wrap also had like charges and repelled each other. Since the wool-rubbed balloon attracted the plastic-rubbed balloon, students can deduce that these balloons had unlike charges.

Static Electricity

Reading Focus
Suggest that students *take notes* as they read the section headed "Positive and Negative Charges" to help them answer the Reading Focus question.

1. Get Ready

Vocabulary
Science Terms electric charges, static electricity, electric discharge

Support Terms positive, negative, neutral

Background
• Electric charges are responsible for all electrical phenomena. Every substance is made up of minute particles called atoms. These atoms are made up of still smaller particles called electrons, protons, and neutrons. The center of the atom is the dense nucleus, which contains the protons and neutrons. Electrons of an atom travel around the nucleus of the atom. An electron has a negative charge. A proton has a positive charge. Charges of the same sign repel each other; opposite charges attract.

Discussion Starter
• **What do you think happens to a balloon when you rub it with a wool cloth?** Some students may respond that something from the wool cloth was rubbed onto the balloon. Other students will probably say that rubbing the balloon gives it an electric charge.

• **How do you know that the balloon did not have an electric charge before you rubbed it?** Students may respond that the balloon didn't interact with the other balloon until it was rubbed.

Static Electricity

Reading Focus What is static electricity, and how do objects become charged with static electricity?

You're combing your clean, dry hair. Strands of your hair fly away from each other. At the same time, the strands also stick to your comb. In the activity on pages D28 and D29, rubbing balloons with a wool cloth or plastic wrap causes the balloons to be attracted to or repelled by each other. Why does rubbing materials together cause these effects?

Hair, combs, balloons, wool, and plastic are kinds of matter. All matter is made up of tiny particles. Some of these particles carry units of electricity called **electric charges**.

Positive and Negative Charges
An electric charge can be positive or negative. A plus sign (+) stands for a positive charge, and a minus sign (−) stands for a negative charge. Most matter is neutral. A neutral object has the same number of positive charges as negative charges.

Only negative charges can move from one material to another. If negative charges move from one neutral object to another, the first object then has an overall positive charge. The second one has an overall negative charge. Look at the pictures

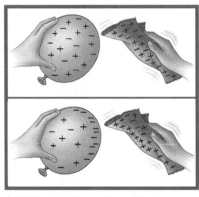

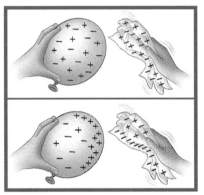

▲ Rubbing a balloon with wool (*top*) gives a negative charge to the balloon (*bottom*). What is the charge on the wool?

▲ Rubbing a balloon with plastic (*top*) gives a positive charge to the balloon (*bottom*). What is the charge on the plastic?

D30

Science & Writing

WRITING STORIES

What to Do Students may enjoy writing adventures or funny stories about static electricity. Perhaps static electricity was instrumental in foiling a fiendish plot to steal magnificent jewels! Or maybe Messy Marvin goes to school with all sorts of things clinging to him, without being aware of them.

What's the Result? As students share their stories, they should be able to describe instances where like charges repelled and unlike charges attracted.

Multi-Age Classroom Groups of students can collaborate on ideas for the story and share the tasks of writing and illustrating.

on page D30. They show balloons becoming charged.

The form of energy that comes from charged particles is called electrical (ē lek′tri kəl) energy. Negative electric charges can move from one object to another. When this happens, an electric charge builds up on both objects. One object will have a positive charge; the other will have a negative charge.

This buildup of electric charges is called static electricity. An object charged with static electricity has a buildup of electric charges on its surface. Objects with a buildup of like charges repel, or push away from, each other as shown in the top picture below.

Recall that when you comb your freshly washed and dried hair, your hair sticks to the comb. When the comb is removed, some of the hairs move away from each other. You're rubbing hair, which is one kind of matter, with plastic, which is another kind of matter.

If the air is dry enough, negative charges move from the hair to the comb, giving the comb an overall negative charge. Since the hair loses negative charges, it now has an overall positive charge. As the bottom picture of the balloons shows, objects having unlike charges attract, or pull toward, each other.

▲ A balloon that has a negative charge repels another one that has a negative charge.

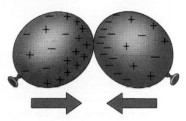

▲ A balloon that has a positive charge attracts one that has a negative charge.

Why do separate strands of the girl's hair repel each other? Why does the comb attract each strand of hair? ▼

D31

on page D30.

Science, Technology & Society

INVENTING

What to Do Challenge students to design an invention that would put static electricity to use. Students can start by listing tasks—such as cleaning up a room or styling hair—that could be accomplished, at least in part, by using static electricity. Encourage students to consider their own experiences with static electricity to develop ideas.

What's the Result? Students' designs should include pictures and written descriptions. Students might build and try out some of their inventions, using common household items.

Multi-Age Classroom Groups of students can collaborate on designs for their inventions, with students sharing the tasks of illustrating their inventions and explaining how they work.

2. Guide the Discussion

Choose from the following strategies to facilitate discussion.

Connecting to the Activities
- *Charge!, p. D28*
- **Why didn't the two neutral balloons in the activity move toward each other or away from each other?** The balloons were neutral before they were rubbed with the wool or the plastic. They had the same number of positive and negative charges. There was nothing to repel them or attract them.
- **In the Investigate Further activity, what happened when you brought a charged balloon close to the puffed cereal grains?** It attracted some cereal grains. **Why does this happen?** The balloon collects a negative charge from the wool. Some electrons from the cereal grains are pushed away, producing a positive charge on the surface of the grains, so that they are attracted to the negatively charged balloon.

Making Inferences
- **How can you tell that an object is charged?** When an object is charged, it either attracts or repels other charged objects.

Thinking Critically
- **If you comb your hair in the dark, you may see sparks. Why does this happen?** Negative charges are rubbed off your hair and move onto the comb.
- **What kind of charge does hair have after negative charges are rubbed off it?** Hair has a positive charge after negative charges are rubbed off.
- **What kind of charge does your comb have after you comb your hair?** It has a negative charge.

Drawing Conclusions

- **If something is negatively charged, does it have only negative charges?** No. Students should conclude that a negatively charged object does not necessarily have only negative charges; it just has more negative charges than positive charges.

- **In the examples on this page, what charge did the socks and shirt have before they were rubbed together in the dryer? What charge did the balloon and wool have before those two were rubbed together?** In all likelihood, all items were neutral. They became charged only after they were rubbed together, transferring negative charges from one item to the other.

Making Inferences

- **Moist air carries charges away from an object better than dry air does. On what kind of a day are you most likely to have "fly-away" hair?** A person is most likely to have "fly-away" hair on a winter day, when there is an increased use of dry heat, causing decreased humidity in the air.

Thinking Critically

- **Suppose there are five balloons sticking to a wall because of static electricity. Is the whole wall charged?** No, only the part of the wall next to each balloon is charged.

- **How can you use what you've learned about static electricity to play a version of "Pin the Tail on the Donkey?"** A balloon "tail" can be rubbed and placed on the wall.

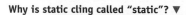

You're taking the laundry out of the dryer, and your socks are stuck to your shirt. This is a case of static cling. Why does this happen?

As the dryer whirls, the clothes rub together. When different materials rub together, negative charges move from some materials to others. So the clothes become charged with static electricity. Your wool socks may have a positive charge and your cotton shirt may have a negative charge. So they attract one another.

When cotton is rubbed with wool, negative charges move from the wool onto the cotton. The cotton then has more negative charges than positive charges. And the wool has more positive charges than negative charges. So both socks and shirt become charged with static electricity.

Attracting Neutral Objects

If you charge a balloon by rubbing it with wool, the balloon may stick to a wall. But the wall is neutral. In the

Why is static cling called "static"? ▼

▲ What evidence is there that the charge on the balloon is the opposite of the charge on the wall?

D32

---

activity on pages D28 and D29, the balloons that stick together are both charged. Why does a charged balloon stick to a neutral wall?

The rubbed balloon has extra negative charges that repel the negative charges in the wall. As a result, that part of the wall has extra positive charges. These charges attract the negative charges of the balloon. So the balloon sticks to the wall.

Shock, Spark, and Crackle

Do you want to shock a friend? Walk across a rug and touch your friend's hand. Your friend may get a mild electric shock. There's a catch, though. You'll feel the shock, too. You may even see a spark and hear a slight crackling sound.

What causes the shock, the spark, and the crackle? When you rub your shoes against the rug, negative charges move from the rug onto your shoes. The charges move from your shoes onto your body. Your body is now charged with static electricity.

Charges that build up in this way don't stay on the charged object. Sooner or later the charges move away. Charges may leak harmlessly into the air. Or the charges may "jump" when static electric charges move off a charged object. When that happens, an **electric discharge** takes place.

In an electric discharge, negative electric charges move from a charged object to another object. ▼

Technology Link
CD-ROM

INVESTIGATE FURTHER!

Use the **Science Processor CD-ROM**, *Magnetism and Electricity* (Unit Opening, Shocking Behavior!) to watch a video about the nature of electric charges and static electricity. See what happens when everyday objects become charged.

D33

Technology Link CD-ROM

INVESTIGATE FURTHER!

Students can use the **Science Processor CD-ROM** *Magnetism and Electricity*, Unit Opening Investigation "Shocking Behavior!" to investigate more about electric charges and static electricity. Students view diagrams and pictures that show the movement of charges from a person's hand to a door knob. They see what happens to the negative and positive charges and how objects become charged. Students watch a video that teaches them about shocks and lightning. Students can extend the investigation by exploring "static cling" using the Blank Page template, the Writer, and the Painter tools.

Making Judgments
• **What are some examples of static electricity you've experienced?** Encourage students to evaluate each example their classmates give.

Drawing Conclusions
• Before students read p. D33, ask: **Have you ever received an electric shock? Describe what happened.** Let students describe the circumstances in which they received a shock. Encourage students to look for similarities in each example—walking or moving the body in some way and then touching something.
• **What caused these shocks?** To some degree, students should be able to relate these shocks to the principles of static electricity. They should mention the build-up of charges on the body and the movement of charges when touching an object.

Meeting Individual Needs
For Extra Help Allow students to demonstrate as many of the examples discussed on these pages as possible. They could try rubbing a balloon against their clothes or hair and see if they can make it stick to the wall.

3. Assess Understanding

Students can work in pairs holding two strips of newspaper or tracing paper, about the size of a ruler, together in one hand. They should rub both strips at the same time with the thumb and forefinger of the other hand. Ask them to explain what happens. (The two papers repel each other because they both received the same charge as the result of being rubbed.)

Reading Focus Answer

Static electricity is the building of electric charges. Objects become charged with static electricity when negative charges move from one object to another.

Lightning

RESOURCE
Lightning

Reading Focus How do electric charges cause lightning?

Reading Focus Suggest that students *skim* for the key phrase *causes lightning* as they read page D34 to locate information they will need to answer the Reading Focus question.

1. Get Ready

Vocabulary
Support Terms lightning, thunder, thunderstorm

2. Guide the Discussion

Connecting to the Activities
- *Charge!, p. D28*
- **How is the balloon that was rubbed with a wool cloth like a cloud in a thunderstorm?** Both build up electric charges.

 ### Meeting Individual Needs
Students Acquiring English Have students make a diagram of a thundercloud, showing how charges build up in the cloud. Display the drawings and have the students explain them to the class.

 The number of lightning flashes would be 12 months × 1 flash/3 months = 4 flashes.

3. Assess Understanding

Groups of three or four students can make a model using cotton to show how lightning occurs in a thunderstorm. Look for students' representation of the buildup of charges in the cloud and on the ground.

Reading Focus Answer

Negative charges on a cloud cause positive charges to build up on the ground below. Negative charges from the cloud then jump from the cloud to the ground.

 ### Internet Field Trip
From **www.eduplace.com** students can link to a Web site about how scientists study lightning. A trip log will guide their visit to the site.

 A flash of lightning contains enough electricity to light a 100-watt light bulb for three months. How many flashes would be needed to light a 100-watt bulb for one year?

Zap! Boom! Lightning flashes across the sky. Then thunder cracks. The wind is strong and rain starts pouring down—it's a thunderstorm. You may know that lightning causes thunder. But what causes lightning?

During a thunderstorm, positive charges can build up at the top of a cloud. Negative electric charges build up at the bottom of the cloud. These negative charges at the bottom of a cloud repel negative charges in the ground below. That causes the ground, and objects on the ground, to be positively charged.

When negative charges jump between the cloud and the ground, there's a giant electric discharge, or spark. This spark is lightning.

Lightning Safety

Lightning often strikes the tallest object on the ground. That is why you should never stand under a tree during

D34

Science & Social Studies

 STORM SAFETY

What You Need book on safety procedures, posterboard, markers

What to Do Find a weather map of the continental United States on the Internet and have students look for places where there is lightning activity. Remind students that lightning strikes can be harmful. Encourage pairs of students to research safety information on what to do when caught in an electrical storm. Students can make posters illustrating some of the safety tips.

What's the Result? Display posters in the classroom. Discuss additional safety rules that should be followed in a storm, including keeping fresh batteries in flashlights and radios.

1 Negative charges on a cloud cause positive charges to build up on the ground and the tree.

2 Lightning strikes when negative charges jump from the cloud to the ground or to the tree.

a lightning storm. Also, you should not play in an open field or swim. Take shelter in a building or an enclosed car.

Using lightning rods is another way to increase lightning safety. A lightning rod is a metal rod about 20 cm (8 in.) long. It is attached to the highest point of a structure. Heavy wires connect the rod to the ground. If lightning strikes the rod, electric charges move through the wires safely to Earth. ■

▲ How can you stay safe if you're outdoors when lightning starts?

Internet Field Trip
Visit **www.eduplace.com** to see how scientists are studying lightning.

INVESTIGATION 1 WRAP-UP

REVIEW
1. What is static electricity?

2. How does a neutral object become positively charged?

CRITICAL THINKING
3. How might you use a balloon with a negative charge to find out whether the charge on another balloon is positive or negative?

4. Explain why playing in an open field during a lightning storm is unsafe.

D35

Assessment

Close
the Investigation

INVESTIGATION WRAP-UP

REVIEW
1. A buildup of electric charges
2. A neutral object becomes positively charged when it loses negative charges.

CRITICAL THINKING
3. Use the balloon as a tester. Because it has a negative charge, it will repel another balloon with a negative charge and will attract a balloon with a positive charge. *(Synthesizing, Generating Ideas)*
4. Lightning strikes the tallest object in an area. A child playing in an open field might be the tallest object in the area and, therefore, might attract lightning. *(Synthesizing, Applying, Generating Ideas)*

CHALLENGE

Ask students to rub a balloon on a wool sweater or wool cloth and then stick the balloon to the wall. Ask them to explain what makes the balloon stick to the wall. They will most likely respond that the balloon has an excess of negative charges. Tell them that their answer is right, but ask: **What causes the attraction between the wall and the balloon? How did the wall become charged?** Students should infer that when the extra negative charges on the balloon approach the wall, they repel the negatives charges nearby. The part of the wall nearest the balloon becomes positive and attracts the balloon.

FOLLOWING UP

Baseline Assessment Return to the class list of why the comb was able to pick up the bits of paper. Ask students if they want to add other reasons now that they understand more about static electricity.

Reteaching Discuss the Investigation subconcept with students. Together, create a word web around the central idea of static electricity. Use the Activity Support Master, "Web" on TRB p. 15.

Use *Science Notebook*, TRB p. 50.

Start
the Investigation

Planner

Subconcept Current electricity is a flow of negative charges through a conductor in a closed circuit.

Objectives

- **Make** a circuit that will light a bulb and a switch that will operate the circuit.
- **Experiment** to find out which materials are conductors and which are insulators.
- **Investigate** how electricity flows in circuits.

Pacing 3–4 class periods

Science Terms electric current, electric circuit, switch, conductors, insulators

Activate
Prior Knowledge

Baseline Assessment Have students make a diagram showing what happens after they turn on a light switch. Save their drawings for use in Following Up.

In Investigation 1 you saw that electric charges can move from place to place. In Investigation 2 you will find out how this flow of electricity can be controlled.

Activity

On or Off?

You usually take for granted that flipping on a light switch will turn on a light. What else has to happen for the light to go on? Find out in this activity.

MATERIALS
- dry cell (size D) in holder
- light bulb in holder
- 3 insulated wires (stripped on ends)
- thick cardboard
- 2 brass paper fasteners
- paper clip
- Science Notebook

Procedure

1. Place all the materials listed above on your desk. With your group, **hypothesize** ways you can connect some of the parts to make the bulb light. **Draw** pictures of these ways in your *Science Notebook*.

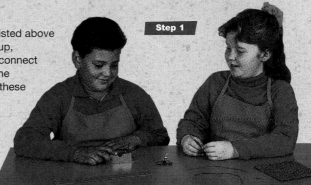

Step 1

D36

Activity On or Off?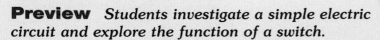

Preview *Students investigate a simple electric circuit and explore the function of a switch.*

Advance Preparation *See p. D26b.*

1. Get Ready

 GROUPS OF 4–6   **50 MINUTES**

Key Science Process Skills hypothesize, experiment, predict, control variables, define operationally

---

👤 Meeting Individual Needs

STUDENTS ACQUIRING ENGLISH

Draw a picture on the chalkboard of the design of the circuit. Be sure to label the diagram and have students repeat key words like *circuit, light bulb, switch, wire,* and *battery* as you point to the different pieces of equipment. Review safety procedures about batteries with students. Encourage students to create sentences describing what happens when the switch is open or closed.

LINGUISTIC

2. **Test** each idea that your group has drawn. Circle the drawings you made that make the bulb light.

3. When the bulb lighted, you had made an electric circuit (sur'kit). An **electric circuit** is a path through which electricity can flow.

4. Use the round picture as a guide to arrange a paper clip, two brass fasteners, and two wires on a piece of thick cardboard.

Step 4

5. You have made a switch, which you can use to turn the bulb on or off. **Make a drawing** to **predict** how you can connect the switch to the circuit. **Test** your prediction. Make sure your drawing shows how the parts are connected when the switch works.

Analyze and Conclude

1. **Compare** your predictions about how to light the bulb—with and without the switch—with your results.

2. An electric circuit through which electricity moves is called a closed circuit. When you disconnect a part of a closed circuit, the circuit is called an open circuit. When you flip a switch to turn on a light, are you opening a circuit, or closing it? Explain your answer.

D37

INVESTIGATE FURTHER!

RESEARCH

What are some different types of switches? How do the switches on electric devices and on the wall work in your home? Why do some switches click and others not click when you turn them on or off? Use resources in a library to find the answers.

INVESTIGATE FURTHER!

RESEARCH

Students may find information about the knife switch, the push-button switch, the key switch, the snap-action toggle switch, and the two-way switch. Most of the switches at home are snap-action toggle switches, in which an insulated handle activates a mechanism that closes or opens the circuit. Turning the switch on connects two metal contacts. Turning the switch off separates two metal contacts. Some switches have mercury contacts that do not click when turned on or off. Students should record their findings on *Science Notebook,* TRB, p. 52.

Materials Hints Caution students not to short-circuit the battery by running a wire from the top to the bottom of the battery.

Safety If a battery or wires become very warm, disconnect the circuit.

2. Guide the Procedure

• Students might get discouraged if they don't have immediate success with the light bulb. Stress the importance of each prediction and trial. Point out that discovering that a certain set-up does not work is as important as finding one that does work. Emphasize that the trial-and-error process is a vital part of science.

• Be sure students take the time to draw each arrangement as they search for one that makes the bulb light.

 Have students record their predictions and answer questions on *Science Notebook,* TRB, pp. 51–52.

 Science Processor Students can use the CD-ROM Painter to make diagrams of workable circuits.

3. Assess Performance

Process Skills Checklist

• Did students **record** each prediction about how to connect the parts of the circuit? Did they draw each arrangement that they tried?

• Did students **control variables** as they tested each prediction?

• Did students **predict** and test how to connect a switch to the circuit? Did they close and open the circuit by moving the paper clip into and out of contact with the paper fasteners?

Analyze and Conclude

1. Students' predictions need not match their experimental results. The bulb will light only if the electricity moves from the dry cell, through the wire to the closed switch, through the closed switch, from the switch through the wire to the bulb, through the bulb, and from the bulb through the wire back to the dry cell. When the switch is eliminated, the current passes through the wires from the dry cell to the bulb and from the bulb to the dry cell.

2. You are closing the circuit when you flip the switch to turn on the light. Only if the circuit is closed can current flow. A bulb can only light if the current is moving through the circuit.

Activity Stop or Go?

Preview *Students experiment with materials that are conductors and those that are insulators, and predict from experimental data which materials belong to each category.*

Advance Preparation *See p. D26b.*

1. Get Ready

 GROUPS OF 4–6   **45 MINUTES**

Key Science Process Skills predict, record and interpret data, infer, define operationally, control variables

Collaborative Strategy Each group member should take turns testing a material. For each trial, a different member should record the results.

Materials Hints Increased current in the circuit will wear the dry cell out faster. The wires should be disconnected from the dry cell after each test.

Safety Review safety precautions with students. To avoid creating a short circuit, the wires attached to the dry cell should not touch each other. In a short circuit the resistance is low, causing the current to increase, thereby heating the wires.

2. Guide the Procedure

- Make sure all connections are secure. Avoid any short circuits. Check all wires to make sure the insulation is not worn.
- Encourage students to make a list of objects that are conductors and insulators other than those mentioned in the activity.

 Have students record their predictions and answer questions on *Science Notebook,* TRB, pp. 53–54.

 Science Processor You may wish to have students use the CD-ROM Spreadsheet to organize and display their data.

Activity
Stop or Go?

Does electricity flow easily through all materials? Try some tests to find out.

MATERIALS
- goggles
- 3 insulated wires (stripped on ends)
- light bulb in holder
- dry cell (size D) in holder
- copper wire
- plastic straw
- penny
- toothpick
- paper clip
- rubber band
- cardboard strip
- aluminum foil strip
- *Science Notebook*

SAFETY
Wear goggles during this activity.

Procedure

1. With your group, use a wire to connect a light-bulb holder to a dry-cell holder. Attach a second wire to the light-bulb holder only. Attach a third wire to the dry-cell holder only. *Do not allow the two wires that are attached to the dry cell to touch.*

2. **Predict** what will happen if you touch the free ends of the wires together, as shown. **Record** your prediction in your *Science Notebook.* **Test** your prediction and **record** your results.

3. A material that allows electricity to flow through it is called a **conductor** (kən duk′tər). **Infer** whether the wires in your circuit are conductors. **Record** your inference.

Step 2

D38

Meeting Individual Needs

EARLY FINISHERS

For each material tested, suggest students write a sentence outlining their prediction and another sentence describing the results of the test.

LINGUISTIC

4. A material that does not allow electricity to flow through it easily is called an **insulator** (in'sə lāt ər). **Make a chart** like the one shown. **Predict** which objects in the Materials list are conductors and which are insulators. **Record** your predictions in the chart. Then **test** them and **record** your results.

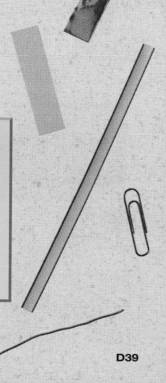

Step 4

Conductor or Insulator

Object or Material	Prediction	Result

See SCIENCE and MATH TOOLBOX page H10 if you need to review **Making a Chart to Organize Data**.

Analyze and Conclude

1. **Compare** your predictions about which materials electricity would flow through with your results.

2. Which of the objects or materials that you tested are conductors? How do you know?

3. Which of the objects or materials that you tested are insulators? How do you know?

UNIT PROJECT LINK

Invent a way to use the opening and closing of circuits to make a quiz board. Work with your group to write a set of questions and answers. Then decide how to place dry cells, wires, and light bulbs. Test your invention by trying it in front of members of other groups in your class.

TechnologyLink
For more help with your Unit Project, go to **www.eduplace.com**.

3. Assess Performance

Process Skills Checklist
- Did students **predict** which materials are insulators and which are conductors? Were students able to reconcile their predictions with their observations?
- Did students **control variables** as they tested each material properly to determine the category to which it belonged? Did students **record** their results in the chart?

Analyze and Conclude
1. Student predictions probably matched the results.
2. The copper wire, penny, paper clip, and aluminum foil strip are conductors. When each of these objects was connected by wires to the dry cell and the light bulb, the bulb lighted. Each of these objects must have allowed electricity to pass through it in a closed circuit.
3. The plastic drinking straw, toothpick, rubber band, and cardboard strip are insulators. When each of these objects was connected by wires to the dry cell and the light bulb, the bulb did not light. Each of these objects must have prevented the flow of electricity, causing the circuit to remain open.

UNIT PROJECT LINK

Tape questions down the left side of a sheet of cardboard and their answers, in scrambled order, down the right side. Place paper clips, one for each question used, down each side. On the reverse side of the sheet, wire each question to its correct answer. Use a light bulb, wire, and battery to create a tester. The bulb should light when the tester connects the paper clip of a question to that of its correct answer. Students can use *Science Notebook,* TRB, p. 55 and Unit Project Masters 2 and 3 on TRB pp. 18–19.

TechnologyLink
Have students visit **www.eduplace.com**. to link with on-line experts who can provide help with the Unit Project.

Electric Current

Reading Focus Suggest that students *skim* the section headed "Changes in Currents" to locate a paragraph that contains information relevant to the Reading Focus question.

1. Get Ready

Vocabulary

Science Terms electric current, electric circuit, switch, conductors, insulators

Support Terms electrical energy, electricity, electric charges, dry cell

Background

• The typical household battery is called a dry cell. It is made of a carbon rod surrounded by a paste of manganese dioxide, ammonium chloride, and carbon powder. The rod and paste are enclosed in a zinc case. Chemical reactions between the paste and the zinc case result in one end of the battery accumulating an excess of electrons, or negative charges, and becoming negatively charged. The other end (which loses electrons into the paste) becomes positively charged. When the battery is connected to a circuit, the excess electrons flow to the carbon rod, setting up an electric current. The chemical reactions in the battery occur until the manganese dioxide is used up. Then the battery is dead.

Discussion Starter

• **How do you use electricity in your daily life?** Encourage as many examples as possible. Students could name large and small appliances that operate from an outlet or from batteries.

• **How would it affect you if you could not use these items for a week?** Let students speculate about what they wouldn't be able to do or what alternative methods they would have to find without electricity. Lead into a more general discussion about how their lives would change without electricity.

Using Math **Students should multiply the number of electric circuits by the number of outlets each circuit has, or $4 \times 6 = 24$.**

Electric Current

Reading Focus What are the parts of an electric circuit?

You press a switch and your flashlight lights or your radio plays music. Electrical energy powers your flashlight and radio. You depend on electricity in hundreds of other ways, too. The picture below shows some ways that electricity works for the members of one family.

Charges in Currents

In Investigation 1 you found out about static electric charges. The charges collect on objects and may jump quickly between objects. But these charges can't be used to run electric devices. For electric charges to be useful, they have to flow.

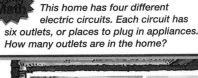
Using Math This home has four different electric circuits. Each circuit has six outlets, or places to plug in appliances. How many outlets are in the home?

D40

Science Around the World

ASWAN DAM

What to Do Throughout the world, dams have been built on rivers to produce electricity. One of the most impressive dam projects is the Aswan High Dam on the Nile River in Egypt. Invite students to research how the dam was built, how electricity is generated there, and how the dam has affected the people of Egypt and the environment near the dam. Encourage students to communicate their findings through posters, diagrams, models, activities, and written and oral reports.

What's the Result? **How has the Aswan Dam affected the lives of the Egyptian people? What effect did it have on the environment?** Students should recognize that the project has both positive and negative aspects.

In the form of electricity used in homes and businesses, electric charges flow steadily, somewhat like currents of water in a stream. An **electric current** is a continuous flow of negative charges. An **electric circuit** is a path along which negative charges can flow. The activity on pages D36 and D37 shows how to put together the parts of an electric circuit.

A simple electric circuit starts with a source of electric charges, such as a dry cell. A wire connects the source to a light bulb or another device. A second wire connects the bulb or the other device back to the source of negative charges.

Open and Closed Circuits

When a circuit is closed, or complete, there is no break in the pathway of negative charges. The charges can flow through a closed circuit. In a closed circuit containing a light bulb, the bulb lights.

When a circuit is open, or incomplete, there's a break in the pathway. Charges can't flow through an open circuit. If you disconnect a wire in a simple circuit, the bulb can't light.

A **switch** is a device that opens or closes a circuit. When you turn a switch to *on*, you close a circuit so it is complete. When you turn a switch to *off*, you open a circuit so it is incomplete. If you add a switch to a circuit, you don't have to disconnect a wire to open the circuit.

▲ Trace the path of electric charges in this circuit. Start and end at the dry cell. Why does the bulb light?

▲ This circuit contains a closed switch. Trace the path of the charges through this circuit. Why does the bulb light?

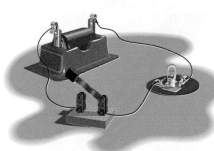

▲ How is this circuit the same as the one in the middle picture? How is it different? Why doesn't the bulb light?

D41

Integrating the Sciences

LIFE SCIENCE

What to Do Direct students' attention to the three diagrams on page D41. Ask: **How do these circuits resemble an organism's systems?** Students should point out that each circuit is made of parts that work together to accomplish a task. Ask students to think of systems related to plant, animal, and human life. Students can illustrate a system and label its parts.

What's the Result? Ask students what might happen if a part of their system were missing or not working properly. Help students understand the importance of each part of a system.

Multi-Age Classroom Groups of students can collaborate on this activity and share the tasks of choosing a system to illustrate, drawing the system, and labeling the parts.

---

2. Guide the Discussion

Choose from the following strategies to facilitate discussion.

Connecting to the Activities
- ***On or Off?, p. D36***
- **How did you know when the circuit was closed in the activity?** The circuit was closed when the light bulb lighted.
- **Did negative electric charges flow through the wires when the circuit was open or closed?** Students should recall that the negative charges flowed through the wires when the circuit was closed.

Making Comparisons
- **How is an electric circuit like a circle of people passing a ball to one another?** The continuous flow of the ball is like the flow of negative charges.
- **How must the ball be passed in order for the circuit to act like an electric circuit?** The ball must pass from one person to another in one direction around the circle; it should not be reversed or passed across the circle in a haphazard way.
- **Is this circuit open or closed?** Closed
- **How would you change the circle of people passing the ball to show an open circuit?** One person could step out of the circle. Assuming the ball can only be tossed with enough force to get it to the adjacent person, the ball would not make it to the next person in the circle, and the circuit would be incomplete, or open.

Meeting Individual Needs

Inclusion Let a group of students model the comparison of a closed and open electric circuit with a group of people playing ball by passing a ball around in a circle. Ask the suggested questions (see above) of the rest of the class as students perform the activity.

Making Inferences

- **Why do you think the cords on electrical appliances are covered?** Students should infer that the covering, acting as an insulator, protects people from touching the wire and being hurt.

Meeting Individual Needs

Students Acquiring English Let groups of students examine the parts of a flashlight. Compare the flashlight with the drawings on p. D43. Name each part as you discuss its importance in a system to produce light. Have students trace the circuit in the flashlight with their fingers.

3. Assess Understanding

Students may work together in groups of three or four to prepare a short segment for a television show that will explain the concept of current electricity to younger children.

Reading Focus Answer

The parts of an electric circuit are a source of electric charges, such as a dry cell, a wire that connects the source to a light bulb or other device, and a wire that connects the device back to the source.

Conductors and Insulators

Have you ever tried running through water? It's hard work, isn't it? Running through air is a lot easier. Electricity also moves more easily through some materials than others.

In the activity on pages D38 and D39, materials are tested for their ability to conduct electricity. Materials that allow electricity to pass through them easily are called **conductors**. Most kinds of metals are good conductors of electricity. Copper is a metal that is used in wires in electrical cords. The wires in the power lines that bring electricity to your house are copper wires, too.

Insulators are materials that don't let electricity move easily through them. Plastics, rubber, wood, paper, cloth, and ceramics are good insulators. The picture shows how a conductor and an insulator are used in an electrical cord.

How a Flashlight Works

What happens inside a flashlight when you turn it on or off? When you turn the switch to *on*, you close the circuit and the bulb lights. When you turn the switch to *off*, you open the circuit, so the light in the bulb goes out. The picture on page D43 shows what's inside one kind of flashlight and how it works.

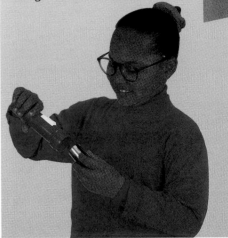

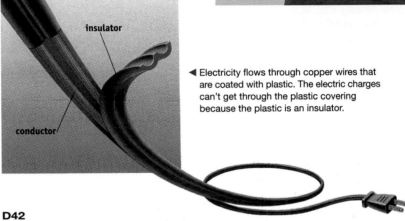

insulator

conductor

◄ Electricity flows through copper wires that are coated with plastic. The electric charges can't get through the plastic covering because the plastic is an insulator.

D42

Science & Math

GRAPHING

What to Do In small groups, have students load three flashlights, one with general purpose batteries, the second with heavy-duty batteries, and the third with alkaline batteries. All batteries should be the same brand, and all bulbs and batteries should be new. To determine which battery is the most economical, students should operate the flashlights until the batteries wear out and lights dim. If necessary, students can take flashlights home to keep them operating.

What's the Result? Construct a bar graph for each kind of battery that shows (1) the operating time (or average operating time), (2) cost, and (3) minutes of operation per penny. Students will likely find that alkaline batteries are the most economical.

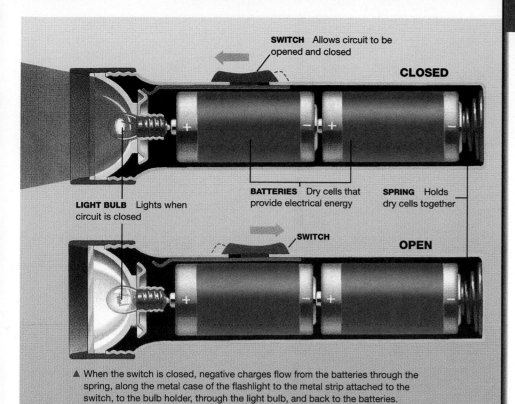

SWITCH Allows circuit to be opened and closed

CLOSED

LIGHT BULB Lights when circuit is closed

BATTERIES Dry cells that provide electrical energy

SPRING Holds dry cells together

SWITCH

OPEN

▲ When the switch is closed, negative charges flow from the batteries through the spring, along the metal case of the flashlight to the metal strip attached to the switch, to the bulb holder, through the light bulb, and back to the batteries.

─── INVESTIGATION 2 WRAP-UP ───

REVIEW

1. Make a sketch of a simple electric circuit. Label the parts.

2. Distinguish between conductors and insulators.

CRITICAL THINKING

3. The bulb in a circuit is not glowing. The circuit consists of a light bulb, switch, dry cell, and three wires. What parts of the circuit would you check to find out why the bulb is not glowing?

4. Suppose you set up a circuit, using a plastic paper clip for a switch. Will the circuit work? If not, how could you get the circuit to work?

D43

═ Assessment ═

Performance

Demonstrate Ask students to use the materials from the activity on p. D36 to demonstrate a closed circuit. Students should be able to tell you what is happening in a closed circuit (negative charges are flowing) and how they know the circuit is closed (the bulb lights).

Investigation Review ▶
Use Investigation Review p. 123 in the *Teacher Resource Book*.

Investigation Review

Circle the word or words that best complete each sentence.

1. Electric charges must (remain still, (flow)) to be useful.

2. An electric current is a stream of ((negative) positive) charges.

3. Charges move through a circuit that is ((closed,) open).

4. Electricity passes easily through (insulators, (conductors)).

5. Electricity powers a (faucet, (flashlight)).

6. Read the steps that describe the movement of electric charges in a closed circuit. The steps are not in the right order. Number them in the correct order.

_4_ Charges move through the light bulb.

_5_ Charges move through the wire leading back to the dry cell.

_1_ Charges leave the dry cell.

_2_ Charges move through the switch.

_3_ Charges move from the switch to the light bulb.

Process Skills
Predicting

What will happen to a buzzer connected to an open circuit? Explain your answer.

The buzzer will not buzz, since electricity won't flow through the circuit.

Close
the Investigation

INVESTIGATION WRAP-UP

REVIEW

1. Student drawings should include wires connecting a dry cell, switch, and light bulb so that electricity can pass through each one of the items and make a complete circuit. Each item should be labeled.

2. Conductors are materials that allow electricity to pass through them easily. Insulators are materials that do not let electricity pass through them easily.

CRITICAL THINKING

3. Student responses will vary but might include (1) that the connection of the wires to the terminals should be checked to be sure the wires are secure; (2) that the lightbulb should be checked to make sure it is firmly in its socket and the filament of the bulb is not broken; and (3) that the switch is closed. **(Applying, Solving Problems)**

4. Because plastic is an insulator, it is unlikely the circuit will work. Students should suggest replacing the plastic paper clip with a conductor such as a metal paper clip. **(Applying, Solving Problems)**

CHALLENGE

Bring in a light switch and allow students to take it apart to see how moving the switch opens and closes a circuit. Have available a copy of David Macaulay's *The Way Things Work* (Houghton Mifflin, 1988), open to "Two Way Switch." Students can compare this switch with the one they made in the activity on p. D36 and share their findings with their classmates.

FOLLOWING UP

Baseline Assessment Return to students' diagrams showing what they think happens after they turn on a light switch. Ask if they would like to refine the diagram now that they know more about electric circuits.

Reteaching Use one of the setups from the activity on p. D36 to review the parts of a circuit, the results of an open and closed circuit, and the path negative charges take through a closed circuit to make a bulb light.

Use *Science Notebook*, TRB p. 56.

Start
the Investigation

How Do Electric Circuits Differ?

pages D44–D52

Planner

Subconcept Electric circuits can be put together in series or in parallel.

Objectives

- **Predict** and **test** how to make two bulbs light when connected in series and in parallel circuits.
- **Explain** how a light bulb works.
- **Describe** series and parallel circuits.

Pacing 3–4 class periods

Science Terms filament, series circuit, parallel circuit, circuit breaker, fuse

---

Activate
Prior Knowledge

Baseline Assessment Ask: **Why might one type of circuit not work if one of the bulbs is missing while another type of circuit does work?** Save class responses for use in Following Up.

How Do Electric Circuits Differ?

Suppose you want to put up a string of lights for a party, but one bulb is missing from the string. Is this a problem? It depends on how the lights are wired. In this investigation, find out the different ways lights can be wired.

Activity
One Type of Circuit

The activity on pages D36 and D37 shows an electric circuit. In this activity you'll examine an electric circuit more closely.

Procedure

1. On your desk, place a dry cell, three wires, and two light bulbs.

2. Find a way to make both bulbs light at the same time. **Talk with your group** and together **predict** a way to use the materials to light both bulbs at once. In your *Science Notebook*, **draw** a diagram that shows the arrangement of materials for your group's prediction.

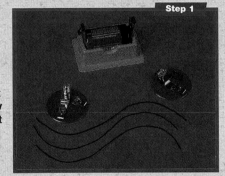

Step 1

D44

Activity One Type of Circuit

Preview *Students experiment with series circuits to light two bulbs and discover that the electricity flows through only one path.*

Advance Preparation *See p. D26b.*

1. Get Ready

 GROUPS OF 4–6   **50 MINUTES**

Key Science Process Skills predict, record data, define operationally, infer

---

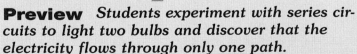
Meeting Individual Needs

STUDENTS ACQUIRING ENGLISH

Students who are acquiring English will especially benefit from making the drawings of each circuit configuration they try. Be sure students properly label each component. Prior to students completing the Analyze and Conclude section, you may want to show them a diagram of a light bulb, complete with a filament. Help them recognize the "circuit". Ask: **What might happen if the circuit is broken?** A light bulb burns out.

VISUAL/SPATIAL

3. Work with your group to **test** your prediction. Make sure that the connections are tight. You may change the connections until both bulbs light. Then **draw** a diagram of your complete circuit.

4. When both bulbs are lighted, **predict** what will happen if you take one bulb out of its holder. **Record** your prediction. **Test** your prediction and **record** your observations.

Analyze and Conclude

1. The circuit you constructed is called a series circuit. In a **series circuit** there is only one path for an electric current. Place your finger on the dry cell in your drawing. Then, with your finger, follow the path of the electric current through the circuit. Use a colored pencil to show this path on your drawing.

2. Would placing a switch between the bulbs in the circuit affect whether one or both bulbs would light? Explain your reasoning. With your teacher's permission, make and test the circuit.

3. Some strings of lights used for decoration are connected in a series circuit. If one light bulb burns out, **infer** what happens to the other bulbs. Why does this happen?

Technology Link CD-ROM

INVESTIGATE FURTHER!

Use the **Science Processor CD-ROM**, *Magnetism and Electricity* (Investigation 3, Power Play) to learn about the connection between electricity and magnets. You can also watch a video about the uses of electromagnetism.

D45

Technology Link CD-ROM

INVESTIGATE FURTHER!

Students can use the **Science Processor CD-ROM** *Magnetism and Electricity*, Investigation 3, "Power Play" to investigate more about the connection between electricity and magnets. Students explore a generator, identify its parts, and learn how it works. Students predict how moving the magnet and changing the number of coils will affect the generator and then manipulate the generator to test their predictions. Students view a scatter plot that summarizes the relationship between the number of coils in the generator and the amount of current. Students can watch a video on electromagnetism and its uses.

Collaborative Strategy One group member might record data, another make drawings of the circuits tried, while others make the connections to form a circuit.

Safety Review safety precautions with students. Remind students not to connect one terminal of the battery to the other with a single wire.

2. Guide the Procedure

- Remind students that the circuit must be closed in order for current to flow.
- Encourage students who are not immediately successful to keep experimenting, trying other configurations.

 Students can record their predictions and answer questions on *Science Notebook,* TRB, pp. 57–58.

Science Processor You may wish to have students use the CD-ROM Painter to make diagrams of their circuits.

3. Assess Performance

Process Skills Checklist
- Did students' **predictions** demonstrate their understanding of circuits? Did they place the second bulb in line with the first?
- Did students **record** their data by drawing each circuit they built?
- Could students **infer** how the results they obtained with series circuits could be applied to other situations?

Analyze and Conclude
1. Students' drawings should include a colored path to show that the current goes from the dry cell through the wire to the first bulb, then from the first bulb through the wire to the second bulb, and then through the wire back to the dry cell. (A drawing of a series circuit appears on p. D50.)
2. Yes. A switch between the bulbs affects whether the bulbs light. If the switch is closed, the circuit is complete, and both bulbs will light. If the switch is open, the circuit is incomplete and neither bulb will light.
3. The other bulbs will not light. In a series circuit, there is only one path through which electric current can travel; everything in the circuit is part of that path. When one bulb is removed, that path is interrupted. Thus, the other bulbs go out.

Activity Another Type of Circuit

Preview *Students investigate how to make a parallel circuit which lights two bulbs and discover that the electricity can flow through more than one path.*

Advance Preparation *See p. D26b.*

1. Get Ready

 GROUPS OF 4–6   50 MINUTES

Key Science Process Skills predict, interpret and record data, define operationally

Collaborative Strategy One group member can record the predictions, another might draw diagrams of the circuits tried, while the others make the connections to construct the circuits.

2. Guide the Procedure

- Point out to students that they must use all four wires to make this circuit.

- As groups succeed in using all materials to make the bulbs light, ask them to trace the path of the current through each of the lights in the parallel circuit. They can compare these separate paths to the single path that went through both lights in the series circuit.

- Encourage students to think back to the circuit that had two bulbs in the series. (You may want to set up a two-bulb series circuit for reference.) Ask: **How does the brightness of the bulbs in the parallel circuit compare with the brightness of the bulbs in the series circuit? Why do you think this is so?** The bulbs in the parallel circuit shine more brightly. Students might infer that in the series circuit the resistance associated with each bulb affects the dimness of the bulbs in the circuit.

 Students can record their predictions and answer questions on *Science Notebook*, TRB, pp. 59–60.

 Science Processor Students can use the CD-ROM Painter to make their diagrams as they experiment to make a parallel circuit.

Activity
Another Type of Circuit

MATERIALS
- dry cell (size D) in holder
- 4 insulated wires (stripped on ends)
- 2 light bulbs in holders
- colored pencils
- Science Notebook

Can you wire a circuit so that one bulb stays lighted when another is missing? Try out your ideas in this activity.

- -

Procedure

1. On your desk, place a dry cell, four wires, and two light bulbs.

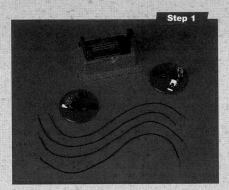
Step 1

2. In the activity on pages D44 and D45, two bulbs are connected in a series circuit. Now you'll connect two bulbs in a different kind of circuit. This circuit will use four wires instead of three. **Talk with your group** and together plan a way to connect the materials. In your *Science Notebook*, **draw** a diagram of your group's plan.

3. Predict how the materials will look when connected so that both bulbs light. Work with your group to **test** your prediction. Make sure that the connections are tight. If you need to, change the connections until both bulbs light. Then **record** your observations.

D46

 Meeting Individual Needs

INCLUSION

Have available a series circuit from the previous activity so that students can compare how the wires are arranged. Direct students to finger trace the path of current through each circuit. Place the circuit on cardboard or posterboard and allow students to trace the circuits in order to obtain a drawing of each circuit.

KINESTHETIC

Step 3

4. When both bulbs are lighted, **draw** a diagram of your complete circuit. Then work with your group to **predict** what will happen to the other bulb if you take one bulb out of its holder. **Record** your prediction and explain why you predicted as you did. Then work with your group to **test** your prediction. **Record** your observations.

Analyze and Conclude

1. The circuit you constructed is a parallel (par'ə lel) circuit. In a **parallel circuit** there is more than one path for an electric current. Starting at the dry cell in your drawing, use your finger to trace each path in your circuit that a current can follow. Use a different-colored pencil for each path in your drawing.

2. Suppose you could choose between a set of lights wired in a series circuit and a set wired in a parallel circuit. Which would you choose? Why?

D47

Process Skills Checklist
* Did students **predict** how to use four wires to connect the two light bulbs to the dry cell to form a complete circuit? Did they test their predictions by connecting their circuits?
* Did students **record** their data by drawing each circuit they built? Were they able to distinguish the drawing of a parallel circuit from that of a series circuit?
* Could students **infer** how the results they obtained with parallel circuits could be applied to other situations?

Analyze and Conclude
1. Students' diagrams should show two separate paths, one through each of the light bulbs. (A drawing of a parallel circuit appears on p. D51.)
2. Students will most likely respond that they would choose the set of lights wired in a parallel circuit because, when a bulb goes out in a parallel circuit, the other bulbs stay lit.

Science & the Arts

ACTING OUT A SKIT

What to Do Encourage students to prepare a skit that shows how series and parallel circuits work. Group members can act out the roles of electric charges, dry cells, conducting wires, and light bulbs in each type of circuit. Individual students can prepare signs that identify their assigned roles and hang the signs around their neck. Then, as groups perform their skits, they should explain how electric charges move through each type of circuit.

What's the Result? The skit should demonstrate how the two types of circuits are alike and how they are different.

The Light Bulb

The Light Bulb

Reading Focus Suggest that students **use a graphic**—a chart—in which they can **compare and contrast** the features of incandescent and fluorescent bulbs.

1. Get Ready

Vocabulary

Science Term filament

Support Terms incandescent, fluorescent, ultraviolet, carbon, tungsten

Background

- A poor conductor resists the flow of electricity. The resistance causes the conductor to heat up when current flows through it. Some poor conductors will get hot enough to glow. Tungsten is the poor conductor used to make the filaments in incandescent bulbs. The tungsten wire is formed into tiny coils. The coils make the filament very long and very thin, so that the filament has a high resistance to electric current. As the filament heats up, some of its atoms give off energy in the form of light. In a light bulb, a tungsten filament can be heated to a temperature of 2,500°C without melting.

Discussion Starter

- **In what ways are a light bulb and a toaster alike?** Students may respond that both a light bulb and a toaster become hot when current passes through them and the wires in each glow when they are hot. Some students may notice each device has coiled wires.

- **What other devices have coiled wires?** Students may have noticed that some portable heaters and ceiling heaters also have coiled wires.

- **Why do you think these wires become so hot?** Some students may suggest that the coils make it difficult for the current to pass through. This heats up the wires and makes them glow.

Reading Focus In what ways are incandescent bulbs different from fluorescent bulbs?

What everyday object turns electrical energy into light? It's a light bulb, of course. Light bulbs come in a number of different sizes, shapes, and colors.

There are bulbs for ceiling fixtures and for table lamps. There are bulbs for street lights, for headlights, and even for growing plants.

Many light bulbs are incandescent (in kən des'ənt) bulbs. Look at the diagram of this type of bulb. As electric current passes through the **filament** (fil'ə mənt), the filament gets so hot that it begins to glow, or give off light.

Now look at the fluorescent (floo-ə res'ənt) bulb. In this bulb, ultraviolet light is changed into white light.

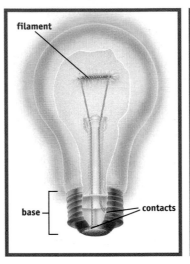

▲ **INCANDESCENT BULB** The filament is a long, thin wire coil made of the metal tungsten (tuŋ'stən). It glows when electricity passes through it. The contacts at the base conduct electricity.

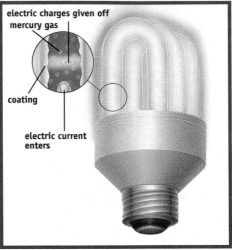

▲ **FLUORESCENT BULB** As electricity enters the bulb, electric charges bump into particles of mercury gas. The gas gives off ultraviolet light. This light strikes the coating, which gives off white light.

D48

Science & Writing

WRITING AN AD

What to Do Ask students to create an advertisement promoting the use of one type of light bulb over another. Suggest that students look at newspaper ads as models and then design their ads on paper or on computer.

What's the Result? Have students discuss the methods they used to persuade people to use fluorescent or incandescent bulbs. Students may have used humor, case studies documenting environmental advantages and energy savings, quotations by celebrities, or other methods.

Multi-Age Classroom Students working in groups can share the tasks of developing persuasive arguments for their ads, designing the ads, and doing the actual drawing and lettering.

INVESTIGATE FURTHER!

RESEARCH

Count the number of incandescent light bulbs in your house. Estimate how long they are used each day. Add together the number of watts for each bulb. Then contact your electric company or an electrical supply store in your community.

Get information about fluorescent bulbs that could replace the incandescent bulbs in your home. Based on the information you obtain, figure out how much money your family could save by switching to fluorescent bulbs.

Thomas Edison (top) and Lewis Latimer (bottom) are shown with an early incandescent bulb invented in the 1870s. About how many years ago was the incandescent bulb invented?

Bulbs and Energy

In incandescent bulbs, electrical energy changes to heat and light. These bulbs produce much more heat than light, so they get very hot. All the heat that incandescent bulbs produce is wasted energy.

In fluorescent bulbs, electricity is used to change one type of light to another. These bulbs produce much less heat and cost less to operate than incandescent bulbs do. Fluorescent bulbs are good for the environment because they don't waste energy.

Invention of the Light Bulb

Thomas Edison, who headed a team of scientists called the Edison Pioneers, invented the light bulb. Edison's first bulb used a filament made of scorched thread. But this bulb was costly and didn't last long.

Lewis Latimer was a member of the Edison Pioneers. Latimer made a greatly improved bulb that used a carbon filament. This bulb cost less and lasted longer than Edison's bulb. Carbon was later replaced by tungsten, which is used in bulbs today. ∎

D49

---

2. Guide the Discussion

Connecting to the Activities

- *One Type of Circuit, p. D44 and Another Type of Circuit, p. D46*
- **What kind of bulb was used in the activities? How do you know?** Incandescent, because the current caused the filament to glow, producing heat and light.

Making Comparisons

- **How are the two basic methods of producing light alike and different?** Both methods cause electrons to produce light. An incandescent light bulb uses electric current to heat a wire filament until it glows. In a fluorescent bulb, electric current causes mercury gas inside the glass tube to emit ultraviolet light, which causes the coating inside the tube to glow.

Identifying and Solving Problems

- Pose this problem to students: **The electric bill for lighting the kitchen has been $1.25 per month. You suggest using fluorescent lights. If it costs only $\frac{1}{5}$ as much to use fluorescent bulbs as incandescent bulbs, how much will your family have to pay each month for lighting the kitchen with fluorescent bulbs?** 25 cents **How much will your family save each month?** One dollar

 Students should respond that the incandescent bulb was invented about 130 years ago.

3. Assess Understanding

Let students work in groups of three or four to survey the lighting in the classroom and, if possible, in other parts of the school. Ask them to create a data table recording the location of each bulb and whether it is incandescent or fluorescent. Students may need a custodian's assistance for this activity.

Reading Focus Answer

An incandescent bulb has a filament that gets hot and glows, giving off heat and light. In a fluorescent light, mercury gas gives off ultraviolet light, which is changed to white light. Incandescent bulbs get hotter and are more costly to operate than fluorescent bulbs.

INVESTIGATE FURTHER!

RESEARCH

With the new styles of fluorescent bulb, which include fuses in the base of the bulb, fluorescent bulbs can be used in nearly any screw socket that accepts an incandescent bulb. A fluorescent bulb uses about $\frac{1}{5}$ the amount of energy as an incandescent bulb producing the same watt output. Therefore, fluorescent bulbs should produce comparable cost savings, particularly for bulbs that are on for an extended length of time. Bulbs that are used for only a few minutes at a time will produce smaller savings. Tell students to record their findings and action taken on *Science Notebook,* TRB, p. 61.

Series and Parallel Circuits

Reading Focus Have students *use the graphic* on page D50 (bottom) to *predict* ways the two kinds of circuits differ. Have them read "Just One Path" and "More than One Path" to *confirm their predictions.*

1. Get Ready

Vocabulary
Science Terms series circuit, parallel circuit, circuit breaker, fuse

Support Terms electricity, circuits, dry cell

Background
• In the activities, students have seen that when they connect two light bulbs in a series circuit, the light in each bulb is dimmer than the light given off by a single bulb. The reason for the dimming is that the resistances of the light bulbs are added together, so the current in the circuit is reduced.

Discussion Starter
• **What problems would arise if the electricity in your home were wired in series instead of in parallel circuits?** Whenever a light bulb burned out, all the electricity in that circuit would stop; no bulbs or appliances would work.

2. Guide the Discussion

Choose from the following strategies to facilitate discussion.

Connecting to the Activities
• *One Type of Circuit, p. D44*
  and Another Type of Circuit, p. D46
• **Which burned more brightly, the light bulbs in the series circuit you made in One Type of Circuit or the bulbs in the parallel circuit you made in Another Type of Circuit?** The bulbs in the parallel circuit burned more brightly.

Series and Parallel Circuits

Reading Focus How do series circuits and parallel circuits differ?

You've seen how electricity flows along paths called circuits. You can compare a circuit's path to a path in a maze. In the two mazes shown below, you start at point *A*, follow some paths, and come back to *A*. You can turn right or left, but you must move only in the direction of the arrows.

In the first maze there is only one path you can follow. You can move from *A* to *B* and then through *C* to get back to *A*. In the second maze there are two paths you can follow to make a round trip. Use your finger to trace these paths.

▲ Trace the path of current through this series circuit.

Just One Path
In the activity on pages D44 and D45, a series circuit is made. A series circuit is one that has only a single path for current to follow. In a series circuit, all of the parts are connected one after the other in a single loop, or path, as shown in the drawing above.

In this circuit, charges flow from the dry cell through bulb *A* and bulb *B* and back to the dry cell. If either bulb is removed from the circuit, the circuit is broken and the current stops.

Mazes that are like two kinds of circuits ▼

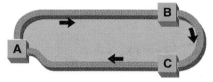

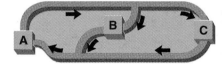

D50

Science, Technology & Society

EXPERIMENTING
What to Do Show how a fuse works. Construct the setup shown. Make the bare-wire sections touch.

What's the Result? A short circuit occurs. The foil fuse melts, opening the circuit and making the light go out.

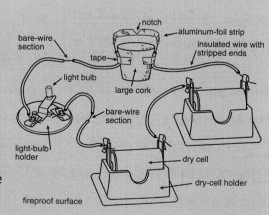

More Than One Path

In the activity on pages D46 and D47, a parallel circuit is made. A **parallel circuit** is one that has more than one path for an electric current to follow, as shown in the picture on the right.

Notice that in path 1, negative charges can flow from the dry cell through bulb A and back to the dry cell. In path 2, negative charges can flow from the dry cell through bulb B and back to the dry cell.

When both bulbs are in place, current will follow both paths, and both bulbs will be lighted. However, if either bulb is removed, current will still

There are two paths a current can follow in this parallel circuit. ▼

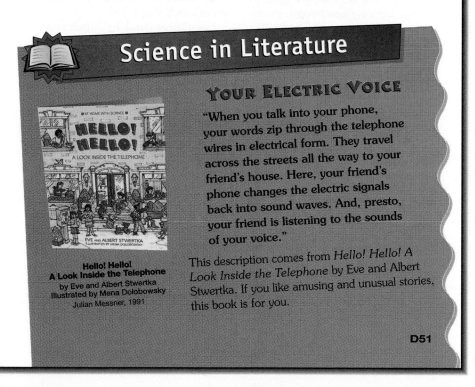

follow the path through the other bulb. So the bulb in this part of the circuit will remain lighted.

Science in Literature

YOUR ELECTRIC VOICE

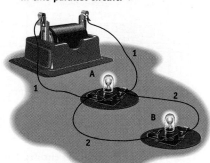

Hello! Hello!
A Look Inside the Telephone
by Eve and Albert Stwertka
Illustrated by Mena Dolobowsky
Julian Messner, 1991

"When you talk into your phone, your words zip through the telephone wires in electrical form. They travel across the streets all the way to your friend's house. Here, your friend's phone changes the electric signals back into sound waves. And, presto, your friend is listening to the sounds of your voice."

This description comes from *Hello! Hello! A Look Inside the Telephone* by Eve and Albert Stwertka. If you like amusing and unusual stories, this book is for you.

D51

Science & Writing

RESEARCHING

What to Do Each student can find out and then write a report about an early scientist who experimented with electricity, such as Alexander Volta, Benjamin Franklin, Hans Oersted, Michael Faraday, Joseph Henry, Thomas Edison, or Lewis Latimer. **How did each scientist use the findings of others and add to our knowledge of electricity?**

What's the Result? Have students share their reports with the class. **How did the work of the scientist you chose contribute to our lives today?** Students' reports should point out various contributions the scientist made to society. **Would anyone argue that society would be better off without some of these contributions?** Encourage discussion.

Making Inferences

- **Is a flashlight an example of a parallel or a series circuit? How do you know?** A series circuit. The two dry cells are in direct contact with the bulb and the metal case. When the switch on the case is open, no current flows. When the switch is closed, a complete path exists and current flows through the circuit.

Transparency 17: Visual/Spatial Activity
Use "Two Kinds of Circuits" to reinforce students' understanding of series and parallel circuits.

Meeting Individual Needs

Inclusion Tell students that the speed with which current flows makes the trip of a negative charge through wires seem almost instantaneous. To provide a clearer picture, slowly move your finger along a drawn circuit on the board. Then ask a volunteer to trace the same path rapidly, making his or her finger a blur.

Science in Literature

Hello! Hello! A Look Inside the Telephone
by Eve and Albert Stwertka

Have students read pp. 24–37 of *Hello! Hello! A Look Inside the Telephone*. Then have them work in small groups to prepare a visual display that illustrates the development of telephone communication from its early stages to the present.

3. Assess Understanding

Let students work in groups of three or four. Ask them to draw a parallel circuit that includes two lamps and a television.

Reading Focus Answer

A series circuit has only a single path for electric current to follow, but a parallel circuit has more than one path for current to follow.

INVESTIGATION WRAP-UP

REVIEW

1. In a series circuit, the electric current has only one path to follow. If part of that path is interrupted, for instance by a missing bulb, the entire circuit is broken. In a parallel circuit, there are places in the circuit that provide separate paths for the electric current. If part of a parallel circuit is broken it is possible for the remainder of the circuit to function.

2. Fuses or circuit breakers open circuits that overheat when too much electricity flows through them. Preventing overheating lessens the possibility of fire.

CRITICAL THINKING

3. If you remove a bulb from a series circuit, you open the circuit because you break the only path through which the current can flow. In a parallel circuit, there are other paths through which electricity can flow. So the removal of one bulb does not break the circuit. *(Synthesizing, Solving Problems)*

4. The switches should each be positioned between the dry cell and a light bulb. *(Synthesizing, Solving Problems, Expressing Ideas)*

CHALLENGE

Have students find out what to do if, when they plug in an appliance, several other appliances stop running. Students should note that they would first make sure all appliances are turned off and then ask an adult to flip the circuit breaker on. Then they should use fewer appliances on that circuit.

FOLLOWING UP

Baseline Assessment Return to the class list of reasons why the bulbs behave as they do. Ask students if they would like to change the list. Look for the addition of series and parallel circuits.

Reteaching How could you be sure that a string of lights was working properly and whether the lights were connected in series or parallel? They could plug the lights in to see if the light bulbs glow. They could then unscrew one bulb. If the rest of the lights remain lit, they are in a parallel circuit.

Use *Science Notebook,* TRB p. 62.

▲ This home has just four circuits, but a real home may have as many as twenty circuits.

How Homes Are Wired

All of the lights and electric appliances in your home are linked in circuits. Lamps, toaster ovens, stereo systems, hair dryers, and refrigerators are parts of the circuits. The circuits in home wiring are parallel, not series. Why, do you think, is this so?

Different circuits control electrical outlets in different parts of a home. Each of these circuits is connected to an outside source of electric current.

One circuit in the house shown above controls the outlets in the kitchen. Trace the circuit that controls the outlets in a child's bedroom.

Every home circuit has a fuse or a circuit breaker. These safety devices open circuits that overheat when too much electricity flows through them. A **fuse** contains a metal strip that melts when overheated. A **circuit breaker** is a switch that opens a circuit by turning itself off. ■

INVESTIGATION 3 WRAP-UP

REVIEW **1.** Compare a series circuit with a parallel circuit.

2. Why do circuits in homes have fuses or circuit breakers?

CRITICAL THINKING **3.** Explain why you can open a series circuit, but not a parallel circuit, by removing one bulb.

4. You want to make a parallel circuit with two light bulbs, a dry cell, and two switches. Draw the way you would connect the parts so that each switch can turn off one bulb at a time.

D52

Assessment

Investigation Review

INVESTIGATION 3 CHAPTER 2

Write the letter of the term that best matches the definition.

<u>d</u> **1.** part of a light bulb that glows   **a.** parallel

<u>f</u> **2.** bulb filled with mercury gas   **b.** fuse

<u>g</u> **3.** bulb that produces two forms of energy   **c.** series

<u>c</u> **4.** circuit connected in a single path   **d.** filament

<u>a</u> **5.** circuit that has more than one path   **e.** circuit breaker

<u>e</u> **6.** switch that opens a circuit by shutting off   **f.** fluorescent

<u>b</u> **7.** device that opens a circuit by melting   **g.** incandescent

Each group of terms below contains one term that does not belong with the others. Cross out the term that doesn't belong.

8. circuit breaker   ~~series~~   fuse

9. ~~carbon~~   parallel   series

10. filament   ~~mercury~~   incandescent

11. fluorescent   ultraviolet   ~~tungsten~~

12. lamps   ~~fuse~~   flashlight

Process Skills
Inferring

Why might the electricity go off in the kitchen of a house if a number of kitchen appliances are running at the same time?

<u>The circuit might be overloaded, causing a circuit breaker or fuse to open the circuit.</u>

Portfolio

Design Using the drawing on p. D52 as a model, students can draw a house, showing how they might wire it using several parallel circuits.

◀ **Investigation Review**
Use Investigation Review p. 124 in the *Teacher Resource Book.*

REFLECT & EVALUATE

Word Power

Write the letter of the term that best matches the definition. *Not all terms will be used.*

1. Circuit that has only one path for electricity to follow
2. Buildup of electric charges on objects
3. Material that lets electricity flow easily
4. A thin wire inside a light bulb
5. Circuit that has more than one path for electricity to follow
6. Safety device that opens a circuit by melting

a. circuit breaker
b. conductor
c. filament
d. fuse
e. insulator
f. parallel circuit
g. static electricity
h. series circuit

Check What You Know

Write the word in each pair that best completes each sentence.

1. A switch that opens a circuit by turning itself off is a (fuse, circuit breaker).
2. A continuous flow of negative charges is an (electric current, electric discharge).
3. A path through which electricity can flow is (a conductor, an electric circuit).
4. A device that opens or closes a circuit is a (switch, cell).

Problem Solving

1. You and a friend are trying to shock each other by rubbing your feet on the carpet. Your friend can shock you, but you aren't able to shock him. Give a reason why this might be so.

2. Suppose that all of the outlets in a room are part of the same circuit. Why is it better to have the outlets wired in a parallel circuit than in a series circuit?

Study the drawing. Explain on paper why the drawing is incorrect. Then make a drawing of a circuit that is correct.

D53

REFLECT & EVALUATE

Word Power

1. h **2.** g **3.** b **4.** c **5.** f **6.** d

Check What You Know

1. circuit breaker **2.** electric current
3. electric circuit **4.** a switch

Problem Solving

1. Rubbing his feet on the carpet allows your friend to build up an electric charge. If you cannot build up a charge by rubbing your feet on the carpet, you may be wearing shoes that are insulators rather than conductors.

2. If there is a break in a parallel circuit, the remaining outlets in the circuit will still receive electricity.

The drawing shows an open switch in a series circuit. If the switch is open, electricity cannot move through the circuit, and the bulb would not light. Students' drawings should show a series circuit with a closed switch.

Assess Performance

Student Task

Have students design an experiment to determine if ten common materials are conductors. Suggest they predict whether or not each material will act as a conductor.

Scoring Rubric

Points	What to Look For
3	Student has a clear plan to test conductivity and includes reasonable predictions.
2	Student's plan is generally workable but some aspects of the plan are not stated clearly.
1	Student's plan is unclear, illogical, and does not test the conductivity of the materials.

Assessment

Chapter Test

Check What You Know Each item is worth 15 points.

For questions 1–4, circle the letter of the correct answer.

1. Darnell rubs two balloons over the wool carpet. What is most likely to happen to the balloons when he holds them close together?
   a. They will pop.
   b. They will repel each other.
   c. They will get bigger.
   d. They will attract each other.

2. Electricity flows through the circuit you see in the diagram. Which of the following materials is most likely to be connected to the free ends of the wires?
   a. aluminum foil
   b. plastic
   c. rubber
   d. cardboard

Problem Solving Each item is worth 15 points.

3. During a thunderstorm, Yolanda saw a bolt of lightning strike a television antenna on a roof. Why do you think the lightning hit the antenna?
   a. The negatively charged antenna attracted positive charges in a storm cloud.
   b. Rain carried electric charges to the antenna.
   c. Negative charges at the bottom of a storm cloud jumped to the positively charged antenna.
   d. Air particles near the antenna heated up, causing sparks.

Chapter Test

4. Mark created a circuit for a science fair. He wanted to be able to open and close the circuit easily without connecting and disconnecting the wires. What device best suited his needs?
   a. a fuse   b. a battery   c. a light bulb   **d.** a switch

5. What kind of circuit, series or parallel, is best for a set of holiday lights? Why?
   A parallel circuit is best. If one light goes out, the others will stay lit, since current has more than one path to follow.

Word Power Each item is worth 5 points.

Use the words in the box to answer each riddle.

electric circuit	fuse	insulator
electric discharge		conductor

6. I am a friend of electricity and allow it to run through me easily. What am I? **conductor**

7. I am the path along which electricity travels. What am I? **electric circuit**

8. I am the crackle you hear when you touch a doorknob after rubbing your feet across a carpet. What am I? **electric discharge**

9. I try to keep electricity from getting to you. What am I? **insulator**

I keep homes safe by opening overloaded circuits. What am I? **fuse**

◀ **Chapter Test**
Use pp. 125–126 in the *Teacher Resource Book*.

CHAPTER 3

ELECTRICITY AT WORK

Subconcepts	Activities	Materials
Investigation 1 What Are Some Sources of Electric Current? pp. D56–D65		

Electric current sources include generators, electric cells, and solar cells.
Suggested Pacing: 5 class periods
National Science Education Standards
   See page D 1c, numbers 3 and 5.
Project 2061 Benchmarks
   See page D 1c, numbers 1 and 4.
	Detect a Current, p. D56
	Science Process Skills: observe, infer, predict, make models
	
	A Magnetic Source, p. D57
	Science Process Skills: infer; collect, record, and interpret data; identify and control variables; define operationally; make and use models
		Detect a Current
		insulated wire (stripped on ends, 50 cm) *, metric tape measure *, compass *, transparent tape, dry cell (size D) in holder *, *Science Notebook,* TRB p. 67
		
		A Magnetic Source
		insulated wire (stripped on ends, 3cm) *, cardboard tube *, current detector from activity on page D56, bar magnet *, *Science Notebook,* TRB pp. 68–69

Investigation 2 How Is Electricity Useful? pp. D66–D76		

Electric current is changed into useful forms of energy in electric devices.
Suggested Pacing: 2–3 class periods
National Science Education Standards
   See page D 1c, numbers 3, 4, and 5.
Project 2061 Benchmarks
   See page D 1c, numbers 1, 2, 5, and 6.
	Make It Move, p. D66
	Science Process Skills: measure and use numbers, infer, predict, identify and control variables, define operationally
		Make It Move
		insulated wire (stripped on ends, 125 cm) *, metric ruler, iron nail *, 10 paper clips *, dry cell (size D) in holder *, *Science Notebook,* TRB pp. 71–72

Name _____

Light Up Your Life

A light bulb changes electricity into light. Electricity passes through the very thin wire, called a **filament**, inside the bulb. As electricity flows through the filament, the wire gets hot and gives off light.

Look very closely at the filament in a light bulb. It is made of tiny coils of wire. By using coils, more wire can be put in the bulb—so more light can be made.

Directions: Label the parts of the light bulb using the words from the Word Bank.

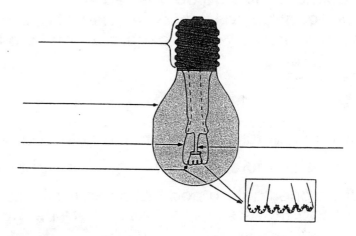

Word Bank

coil filament

glass bulb

wire support

glass support

base

On the top of a light bulb, you will see numbers and letters, such as **60W** or **100W**, or **60 watts** and **100 watts**. This tells you how much power the bulb uses. The more power the bulb uses, the brighter it glows.

1. Which light bulb uses the most electricity? _____

2. Which light bulb would make a good night light in your bedroom? _____

3. Which light bulb would glow the brightest? _____

4. Which light bulb would be a good light for reading? _____

Investigate
The first light bulb ever made had a filament made out of cotton! It burned brightly, but didn't last long. Find out who invented the first light bulb and when it was invented.

Name _____

Series or Parallel?

A

B

You can light several light bulbs with only one cell. In picture **A**, the bulbs are connected in a **series circuit.** What would happen to the circuit if you unscrewed one bulb? All the lights would go out. In picture **B**, the bulbs are connected in a **parallel circuit.** What would happen if you unscrewed a light bulb in a parallel circuit? The other lights would still burn.

Dry cells can also be connected in series and parallel circuits. However, cells are usually connected in series. A series of cells increases the amount of power that flows in a circuit. A series of cells will make a light bulb burn brighter.

C

D
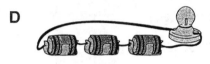

1. In which picture above are the cells connected in a series?_____

2. In which picture above will the bulb light more brightly?_____

3. When one light burned out on Sally's Christmas tree, the rest of the lights went out, too. In what kind of circuit were the bulbs connected?_____

4. Do you think the electric lights in your house are connected in a series circuit or a parallel circuit?_____How do you know?_____
_____

5. How are the batteries connected in the flashlight below? In a series or parallel?
_____

6. Some flashlights have four or five cells. How would the brightness of the light from this kind of flashlight compare with one that has only one or two cells?

Fantastic Fact
A single dry cell is often called a battery, but it really isn't a battery. A battery is two or more cells connected together. You can buy batteries that look like a single cell, but they are really two or more cells connected together and put inside one case.

Overview

In this chapter students will study and investigate electric current and its uses in everyday life.

Chapter Concept

Electric current is produced in generators, electric cells, and solar cells and it can be changed into useful forms of energy.

Theme: Models

Using models of current flow and energy transfer allows students to better understand how electricity is produced, moved, and transformed.

Advance Preparation	Resources/ Vocabulary	Assessment
Detect a Current Cut 50-cm lengths of wire for each group. Strip ends.	**Producing Electric Current** Vocabulary: generator, electric cells	**Chapter 1 Baseline Assessment:** TRB pp. 65–66
		Investigation 1 Baseline Assessment: TG p. D56
A Magnetic Source Cut 3-m lengths of wire for each group. Strip ends.	**From Power Plant to You** Vocabulary: voltage	**Investigation 1 Review:** TRB p. 128 **Think It/Write It:** p. D65; TRB p. 70
	Electricity From Sunlight Vocabulary: solar energy, solar cell	**Following Up on Baseline Assessment:** TG p. D65 **Performance:** TG p. D65
Make It Move Cut 125-cm lengths of wire for each group and strip ends.	**Long Distance, Short Time**	**Investigation 2 Baseline Assessment:** TG p. D66
	Electric Magnets Vocabulary: electromagnet	**Investigation 2 Review:** TRB p. 129 **Think It/Write It:** p. D76; TRB p. 75
	A Car That Plugs In	**Following Up on Baseline Assessment:** TG p. D76
	Safety Around Electricity	**Portfolio:** TG p. D76
		Chapter 1 Summative Assessment Reflect and Evaluate: p. D77 Chapter 2 Review/Test: TRB pp. 130–131 *Science Notebook,* TRB pp. 76–77

*Materials in the Equipment Kit   TG= Teaching Guide   TRB= Teacher Resource Book

Chapter Overview

Concept Preview

You may wish to use Transparency D3 to introduce some of the important concepts of the chapter. Students can add to the map as they complete each Activity and Resource. Then they can use the completed map as a study guide. See below for an example of a completed map.

Vocabulary Development

You may use Vocabulary Master D3 at any point in the chapter to provide additional support for the science vocabulary words.

Common Misconceptions

Students may think a generator or a dry cell contains electricity that it dispenses on demand.

Introducing the Chapter

Warm-Up Activity

 Encourage pairs of students to list all the ways they communicate with other people. Ask them to write a capital E next to each method that uses electricity.

Use *Science Notebook*, TRB pp. 65–66.

Discussion Starter

Initiate a discussion sbout students' current understanding of how electricity works for people, using the photo and text on p. D54.

- **Why is a line worker's job dangerous?** Working with electricity can always be dangerous, but working at such heights, with heavy equipment, and during storms is much more so.

- **What safety precautions might a line worker take?** They use rubber-soled shoes and insulated gloves and tools. They test wires to make sure they are not "live," and they follow other safety guidelines.

CHAPTER
3

ELECTRICITY AT WORK

You turn on the TV set and the picture appears. Where does the electricity come from to make this happen? How does electricity get to your home? What produces this electricity? In this chapter you'll find out the answers to these questions as you explore the story of electricity.

PEOPLE USING SCIENCE

Electrical Engineer Have you ever wondered what makes your telephone work? When Adelina Mejia-Zelaya was a child, she wondered about such things. She wondered how, by just pressing a button, she could make an elevator or a calculator work. Since that time she has studied much about all kinds of electronic equipment.

Today Adlina Mejia-Zelaya is an electrical engineer. Designing tiny electric circuits is part of her everyday work. Explaining her work, she says, "I design circuits for the computers that make your phone work."

In this chapter you'll learn more about electricity. And you'll explore some of the many ways that electricity can be useful.

D54

Concept Preview

Transparency

Sources of Electricity

Generator — Electric Cell — Solar Cell

Generator	Electric Cell	Solar Cell
Energy is produced by using a coil and a magnet.	Energy of motion changes into electrical energy.	Energy is stored in chemicals.	Chemical energy changes into electrical energy.	Uses the energy of the Sun.	Sunlight changes into electrical energy.

Two kinds

Wet cell — Dry cell

Vocabulary Development

Vocabulary Master

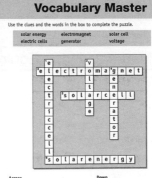

Use the clues and the words in the box to complete the puzzle.

solar energy   electromagnet   solar cell
electric cells   generator   voltage

Across
3. A magnet made when an electric current passes through a wire coiled around an iron core
5. A device that changes light into electrical energy
6. The energy of the sun

Down
1. A battery is made up of one or more of these smaller parts that change chemical energy to electrical energy
2. The force that pushes electricity along wires
4. A device in which a wire coil and a magnet are used to produce electricity

▲ Reading Support Book
Transparency D3

▲ Reading Support Book
Vocabulary Master D3

WHAT ARE SOME SOURCES OF ELECTRIC CURRENT?
.... D56

HOW IS ELECTRICITY USEFUL?
.... D66

Electrical engineer Adelina Mejia-Zelaya works with tiny electric circuits, such as these.

D55

Chapter Road Map

WHAT ARE SOME SOURCES OF ELECTRIC CURRENT?

Activities Detect a Current*, A Magnetic Source*

Resources Producing Electric Current*, From Power Plant to You, Electricity From Sunlight

HOW IS ELECTRICITY USEFUL?

Activities Make It Move*

Resources Long Distance, Short Time, Electric Magnets*, A Car That Plugs In, Safety Around Electricity*

* Pressed for Time?

If you are pressed for time, focus on the Activities and Resources identified by this clock.

Home-School Connection

Distribute the Explore at Home Activity "Safety First" (Teacher Resource Book, page 6) to students after they have completed the chapter.

Technology Link

CD-ROM

Science Processor *Magnetism and Electricity*

To enhance or replace Investigation 1, use **Power Play.**

Using activities in **Power Play**, students examine the relationship between magnetism and electricity. They experiment with a simple electric generator, observing its components—a magnet that moves through a coil of wire to produce electric current. Students explore how the number of coils affects the amount of current produced. They input their hypotheses in the Science Notebook and record their observations on a Spreadsheet. Then they watch a video about ways that electromagnetism is used.

Correlation to AIMS

If you use AIMS Activities, you may wish to use the activity Make a Galvanometer on pages 63–64 in the *Electrical Connections* book to further explore electric currents.

Start
the Investigation

Planner

Subconcept Electric current sources include generators, electric cells, and solar cells.

Objectives
- **Make** and **use a model** of a galvanometer and an electric generator.
- **Explain** how power plants produce electricity.

Pacing 5 class periods

Science Terms generator, electric cells, voltage, solar energy, solar cell

Activate
Prior Knowledge

Baseline Assessment Help students make a word web that shows the items students think are needed to make electricity. Save the web for use in Following Up.

WHAT ARE SOME SOURCES OF ELECTRIC CURRENT?

You've seen that electricity can flow through wires. A dry cell provided a source of energy for that current. In this investigation you'll find out about some other sources of electrical energy.

Activity
Detect a Current

How can you tell if a current is flowing in a wire? Make a current detector.

MATERIALS
- insulated wire (stripped on ends, 50 cm)
- metric tape measure
- compass
- transparent tape
- dry cell (size 0) in holder
- *Science Notebook*

Procedure

Starting from the middle of a 50-cm wire, wrap several turns of wire around a compass so that the wire is either parallel to the compass needle or forms a narrow **X** with the compass needle. Tape the wire in place. You've made a current detector. Connect one end of the wire to a dry cell. With your group, **predict** what will happen when you connect the free end of the wire to the dry cell. **Test your prediction** and **record** your observations in your *Science Notebook*.

Analyze and Conclude

1. What happens when a current flows through the wire?
2. **Infer** what causes any changes you observe.

D56

Activity Detect a Current

Preview *Students focus on one way to detect an electrical current by making a model galvanometer.*

Advance Preparation *See p. D54b.*

1. Get Ready

 GROUPS OF 4–6   **20 MINUTES**

Key Science Process Skills predict, observe, record data, infer

Multi-Age Strategy Some students might be more adept at assembling and others more adept at recording observations.

2. Guide the Procedure

- Check students' detectors. The wire and compass needle should form a narrow X or be parallel to each other.

Have students record their observations and answer questions on *Science Notebook,* TRB, p. 67.

3. Assess Performance

Process Skills Checklist
- Did students accurately **make a model** of the current detector?

Analyze and Conclude
1. The compass needle moves.
2. The electric current caused the compass needle to move.

Activity

A Magnetic Source

How can you use your current detector to find another source of electric current?

Procedure

1. Wind 3 m of wire into a coil around a cardboard tube. Leave about 25 cm of wire free at each end of the tube, as shown. Then put your current detector from the activity on page D56 on your work surface.

Step 1

2. **Talk with your group** and **infer** whether or not there is an electric current in the wire coil. **Record** your inference in your *Science Notebook*. Then **test** your inference by connecting the free ends of the current detector to the free ends of the wire coil. **Record** your observations.

3. Now **predict** how a magnet moving inside the tube might affect your current detector. **Record** your prediction. Then **test** it by moving a bar magnet back and forth quickly inside the tube. **Observe** the current detector when the magnet is moving and when it is still. **Record** your observations.

Step 3

4. Now try holding the magnet still and moving the tube back and forth. **Record** your observations.

Analyze and Conclude

1. **Infer** what caused the electric current in this activity. What observations support your inference?

2. The device you made with a wire coil and a magnet is called a **generator** (jen'ər āt ər). How might a generator be used to make an electric current?

Meeting Individual Needs

GIFTED AND TALENTED

Have students predict what will happen if they switch the wire connections in their current detectors. Let them test their predictions. Students will discover that if the wire connections are reversed, the compass needle will point in the opposite direction, indicating that the current is flowing in the opposite direction.

LOGICAL/MATHEMATICAL

Activity   A Magnetic Source

Preview *Students focus on using a bar magnet to produce an electric current.*

Advance Preparation *See p. D54b.*

1. Get Ready

 GROUPS OF 4–6   **25 MINUTES**

Key Science Process Skills infer, define operationally, identify variables

Collaborative Strategy Since the deflection of the compass needle will be very small, one student should carefully observe the compass while another student moves the magnet.

2. Guide the Procedure

- Using a longer piece of wire (5–6 m) and more coils will produce a stronger current that will be easier to detect. Use new, strong bar magnets if possible.

 Have students answer questions on *Science Notebook*, TRB, pp. 68–69.

3. Assess Performance

Process Skills Checklist
- Can students **identify** the moving magnet as a manipulated variable?
- Did students **infer** that a magnet moving through a wire coil can produce a current?

Analyze and Conclude

1. Students should suggest that either spinning a magnet inside a wire coil or spinning a coil around a magnet could generate an electric current. The compass needle did not move when the detector was connected to the stationary wire coil or when the magnet was not moving in and out of the coil.

2. The electric current produced by a generator can pass through wires to the point where electricity will be used.

Producing Electric Current

Producing Electric Current

Reading Focus How do generators and electric cells produce electrical energy?

Where do you get the energy to kick a soccer ball? You get energy from food. Suppose you eat a peanut butter sandwich. The sandwich—and everything else you eat—has chemical energy stored in it. Your body can change that chemical energy into energy of motion.

Electricity From Magnetism

Energy of motion can change to electrical energy. In the activity on page D57, moving a magnet inside a wire coil produces an electric current in the wire. Moving a wire coil in a magnetic field will also produce a current in the coil.

A device in which a wire coil and a magnet are used to produce electricity is called a **generator**. A generator is a device that changes energy of motion into electrical energy.

Getting a Strong Current

The magnet used in the activity is not very strong. And not many turns of wire are used to make the coil. With a current detector you can detect a current produced by such a generator.

But the current isn't even strong enough to light a bulb. How can a stronger current be made?

The stronger the magnet in a generator, the stronger the current produced. Adding more turns of wire to the coil also strengthens the current. So you could make your generator stronger by using a strong magnet and many coils of wire.

Giant generators produce the electricity that flows to the electrical outlets in homes and schools. These generators also produce the electricity that lights cities, powers machinery, and works in other ways. The generators have powerful magnets and huge coils of wire.

Where does the energy of motion that turns large generators come from? The energy may come from a power plant that uses coal or nuclear fuel to heat water. The heated water makes steam, which turns the generator. Sometimes the energy comes from water falling over a dam such as the one shown on the next page. Or the energy may come from wind turning the blades of a windmill.

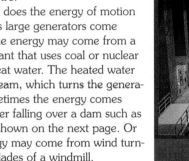

Reading Focus

Reading Focus Suggest that students *monitor* their reading, stopping at intervals to ask themselves if they need to reread or ask for help to understand information that will help them answer the Reading Focus question.

1. Get Ready

Vocabulary

Science Terms generator, electric cells

Support Terms chemical energy, windmill, battery

Background

• Thomas Alva Edison was the first entrepreneur to set up an industrial-research laboratory. Through his efforts, as well as the efforts of the machinists, drafters, mathematicians, and others in his employ, Edison was able to produce numerous inventions. Among these were carbon transmitters, a then "modern-day" generator, the incandescent light bulb, a railroad system powered by electricity, and the first commercial lighting and power company. Edison and his research group are also credited with developing the alkaline storage battery, which provided a source of electricity to run his famous phonographs, and, eventually, to provide power to start cars. In his lifetime, Edison acquired nearly 1,000 patents—34 for the telephone, 141 for the alkaline storage batteries, 150 for the telegraph, 195 for the phonograph, and 389 related to power and electric lights.

Discussion Starter

• **Describe how you think energy of motion can be changed to electrical energy.** Students should be able to describe, based on their observations and results from the first activity, that moving a magnet in and out of a coil of wire (energy of motion) can produce electricity.

• **How would you go about building an electric generator for your home?** Allow students to speculate on methods they might employ to produce electric current for their home.

Integrating the Sciences

LIFE SCIENCE

What You Need magazines, scissors, tape, posterboard, markers or pencils

What to Do Point out that energy can change form; it cannot be created or destroyed. Remind students that the energy they need to move comes from the foods they eat. Ask students to sketch or cut pictures of people "in action" and foods from magazines. Have them use the pictures to make a diagram that shows how energy stored in foods is changed into energy of motion.

What's the Result? Diagrams should show how energy moves from one source to another. For example, arrows might connect pictures to show how energy moves from the Sun, to grass, to a cow, to milk, and finally to a person running.

Using Math
Hoover Dam is 201 m (660 ft) thick at its base and 14 m (45 ft) thick at its top. How much thicker is Hoover Dam at its base than at its top?

Hoover Dam stands in the Black Canyon of the Colorado River. Water falling over the dam provides energy to turn large generators.

▲ Power plant at Hoover Dam

▲ Generators inside the power plant at Hoover Dam

D59

Science & Social Studies

LIFE LONG AGO

What to Do Students can work in groups of three or four to research and then write a short story that describes a typical day in a family's life prior to the widespread use of electricity.

What's the Result? Groups can use simple props to reenact their stories for other groups. For example, students might show how people depended on candles for reading, wood for cooking and heating, paper fans for cooling themselves on hot days, and ice boxes for food storage, among others. **Identify four devices you use regularly that use electricity.** Responses might include hair dryers, electric stoves, microwave ovens, lights, computers, and refrigerators.

2. Guide the Discussion

Choose from the following strategies to facilitate discussion.

Transparencies 18 and 1: Visual/Spatial Activity
Use the transparency "Generating Electricity" along with the "Moiré Overlay" transparency to reinforce students' understanding of how electricity is produced in a power plant.

Connecting to the Activities
• *A Magnetic Source, p. D57*
• **Imagine that you glued a large magnet into a tube around which you put a wire coil with 1,000 turns. Will your coil and magnet generate electricity? Why or why not?** No; the magnet is glued and so cannot move in and out of the coiled tube, so electricity will not be generated.
• **How would you change the coil and wire setup in the activity so that it would produce a greater current?** Students should recognize that increasing the number of turns in their wire coil would increase the amount of current they could generate.

Math Hint *Students should compute that Hoover Dam is 187 m (615 ft) thicker at its base than at its top.*

Meeting Individual Needs

For Extra Help Students can make drawings to summarize how electricity is generated. Students should draw one device or component on each of seven index cards: coal, a waterfall, a turbine, an electric current, steam, wire coils, and a magnet. Have students arrange the cards in the proper sequence and then describe what part each device or component plays in the generation of electricity.

Students Acquiring English Help students use dictionaries to form a list of perhaps more familiar synonyms for the word *generate*. Words might include *produce, make, start, create,* and so on.

Transparency 19: Visual/Spatial Activity

Use the transparency "Wet Cell" and have students trace the path of the current.

Making Comparisons

- **How are coal, nuclear, moving-water, and wind power plants the same? How are they different?** All four are sources of energy that can be converted to electrical energy by generators. They are different in many ways, including how they create the motion needed to turn the generator: coal and nuclear fuels heat water to make steam to turn the generator, while water and wind turn the generator by their constant movement.

- **How are wet and dry cells alike? How do they differ?** Both are electric cells that change chemical energy into electrical energy. Both use two different metals to produce electricity. In a wet cell, a liquid completes the circuit. In a dry cell a paste completes the circuit.

Meeting Individual Needs

Students Acquiring English Using the illustration on this page, have students use an index finger to trace the path of the current as you slowly describe how an electric current flows through a wet cell.

Gifted and Talented Challenge students to construct a wet cell using a lemon with slits cut in it, a zinc strip and a copper strip (each with a hole in one end) and the current detector from the activity on page D56. Students can use the illustration on page D60 as a guide to construct their wet cell. Caution students that the zinc and copper strips should be close to—but not touching—one another. Once students have constructed their wet cell, they can describe it to their classmates, indicating how they know electricity is flowing through the circuit.

Chemicals and Currents

Batteries are another source of useful electrical energy. A battery is made up of one or more smaller parts called **electric cells.** Energy is stored in chemicals used in an electric cell. When an electric cell is connected to a circuit, this stored chemical energy changes into electrical energy.

There are two basic types of electric cells—wet cells and dry cells. The drawing below shows the operation of a simple wet cell. In this wet cell, strips of the metals copper and zinc hang from the wires of a current detector into a liquid chemical. The zinc metal reacts with substances in the liquid to produce a chemical change. This change separates negative charges from zinc atoms.

The negative charges move through the zinc strip, which then becomes the negative end of the cell. These charges then move through the wire around the current detector to the copper strip. This strip has become the positive end of the cell. As the charges move back into the liquid, the circuit is completed.

A WET CELL

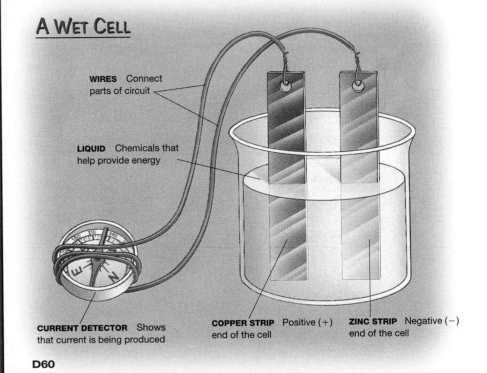

WIRES Connect parts of circuit

LIQUID Chemicals that help provide energy

CURRENT DETECTOR Shows that current is being produced

COPPER STRIP Positive (+) end of the cell

ZINC STRIP Negative (−) end of the cell

D60

Science & Writing

WRITE AD COPY

What to Do Invite students to write copy for a mail-order catalog of environmentally friendly products. The ads should describe a battery charger that uses solar energy. Students can include a title that suggests how the recharger is good for the environment.

What's the Result? Students could share their copy with the class, examine each for appealing content, and infer which battery charger might be best for the environment.

Multi-Age Classroom Students could work on catalog copy in small groups. Encourage each member of a group to suggest at least one idea to use in their catalog title. All group members should agree on the final title.

A dry cell like the one used in the activity on page D56 is shown below. Trace the path of charges through the cell and around the current detector.

A zinc case is the negative end of the cell. A chemical paste inside the case has a carbon rod in its center. The carbon rod is the positive end of the cell. Zinc reacts with substances in the paste, separating negative charges from the zinc atoms. These charges move through the wire around the current detector to the carbon rod and back to the paste, completing the circuit. ■

Technology Link
CD-ROM

INVESTIGATE FURTHER!

Use the **Science Processor CD-ROM**, *Magnetism and Electricity* (Investigation 3, Power Play) to experiment with an onscreen magnet and coil. From the same program, you can learn more about the parts of a generator and how a generator works.

A DRY CELL

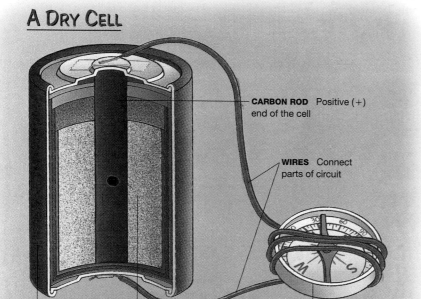

CARBON ROD Positive (+) end of the cell

WIRES Connect parts of circuit

ZINC CASE Negative (−) end of the cell

PASTE Chemicals that help provide energy

CURRENT DETECTOR Shows that current is being produced

D61

Technology Link CD-ROM

INVESTIGATE FURTHER!

Students can use the **Science Processor CD-ROM** *Magnetism and Electricity*, Investigation 3, "Power Play" to experiment with an onscreen magnet and coil. Students explore the parts of a generator and learn about how it works. Students predict how moving the magnet and changing the number of coils will affect the generator and then manipulate the generator to test their predictions. Students view a scatter plot that summarizes the relationship between the number of coils in the generator and the amount of current. Students can watch a video on electromagnetism.

Transparency 20: Visual/Spatial Activity
Use the transparency "Dry Cell" and have students trace the current.

Thinking Critically

• Explain to students that the paste in a "dead" battery can corrode, or eat through, the zinc case. Ask: **Why should you remove dead batteries from a flashlight, toy clock, or other device?** If the chemical can eat through a metal case, then it might also eat through and ruin parts of the device.

Meeting Individual Needs

Students Acquiring English Challenge students to compare and contrast wet cells and dry cells. Have them build a Venn diagram to organize their thoughts. To check for understanding, have students orally describe their Venn diagrams.

3. Assess Understanding

Small groups of students can work together to compose and present a public service announcement describing what takes place at a power plant. Allow students to choose who will represent the power plant, the fuel, and the current. Suggest that two students may want to take the part of the generator, one for the coil and one for the magnet. Students can describe, in turn, what happens in their part of the process. Suggest students plan their presentations using Activity Support Master "Sequence Chart" (TRB p. 14).

Reading Focus Answer

A generator is a device made a of wire coil and a magnet. Moving a magnet in and out of the coil or moving the coil around the magnet can generate an electric current. Generators change energy of motion into electrical energy. Electric cells contain chemicals that store energy. When an electric cell is connected to a circuit, the stored chemical energy changes into electrical energy

From Power Plant to You

1. Get Ready

Vocabulary
Science Term voltage
Support Terms generator, power lines, volts

Background
• Transformers are used to increase or decrease the voltage of electric current. Students may be familiar with another type of electric device, sometimes called a transformer. This device, more accurately called an AC/DC adapter or converter, allows electrical energy from the wall outlet to power a device, ordinarily run on batteries. Such a converter performs two functions: it reduces the voltage of the AC current and also converts alternating current (AC) from the outlet to direct current (DC), which batteries generate.

Discussion Starter
• **What is the source of the electric current in our classroom?** Ask the school engineer or custodian to take the class on an electrical tour to point out where electric current enters the school, including any observable transformers along the way.

2. Guide the Discussion

Choose from the following strategies to facilitate discussion.

Analyzing Data
• Have students study the drawing. Ask: **Suppose a power line fell outside the home. Would this line be more or less dangerous than a power cord inside the home?** The power line carries many times more voltage than a power cord in the home.

From Power Plant to You

Reading Focus How does the electricity from a power plant reach your home?

Most of the electricity you use is as near as a wall switch or an outlet. When you flip a switch or plug in a cord, the electric current is right there. But the generators in the power plant that make this current may be very far away from your home. How does electricity from power plants get to other places where it's used? Study the drawing below to find out.

The Force of Electricity
The generators in power plants push the electricity through heavy-duty power lines that leave the plant.

WHERE YOUR ELECTRICITY COMES FROM

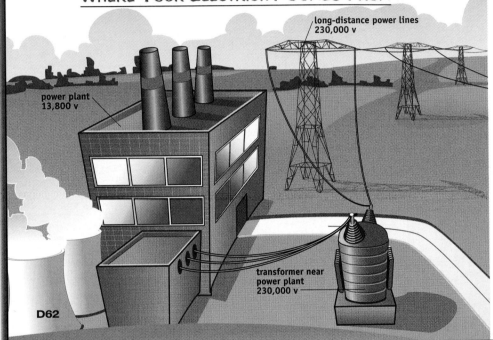

long-distance power lines
230,000 v

power plant
13,800 v

transformer near
power plant
230,000 v

D62

Science, Technology & Society

ENERGY SOURCES
What to Do Suggest students find out the energy sources that power the generators of the local electric company and what percent of the power is generated by coal, hydroelectric, nuclear, solar, or other sources. Then have students determine what percent of the power comes from renewable, nonrenewable, or inexhaustible sources. Students can make two circle graphs to display the information.

Science Processor Have students use the CD-ROM Grapher to make their graphs.

What's the Result? Students should point to their graphs to state their findings.

The force that pushes electricity along wires is called **voltage** (vōl'tij). This force is measured in units called volts. The letter *v* is the symbol for volts.

You can compare voltage to the pressure, or pushing force, of water in a hose. Water can rush from a hose, or flow gently, depending on the pressure. The current in a wire can also be strong or weak, depending on the voltage.

Raising and Lowering Voltage

A transformer (trans fôrm'ər) is a device that changes the voltage of a current. The voltage of the current coming from a power plant is too low to send long distances. A transformer raises the voltage, sending it cross-country to users.

After current makes a long journey from a power plant, its voltage must be lowered. It is too high for use in homes and in most other buildings. So the current is sent through another transformer. Study the drawing to see how voltages are changed as current travels from a power plant to you and to other users of electricity. ■

 How much greater is the voltage at the transformer near the power plant than the voltage at the substation transformer?

home
120 v and 240 v

farm
480 v and 600 v

pole transformers

transformer
at substation
12,000 v

pole transformer

factory
480 v and 600 v

D63

Thinking Critically

- Explain that a 120-volt current is needed to operate most appliances. Ask: **Why does the pole transformer through which current enters a home also supply 240-volt current?** Some appliances, like electric clothes dryers, operate on twice as much voltage as small electric devices.

Meeting Individual Needs

For Extra Help Have students illustrate the analogy between water moving through a pipe and voltage moving charges through a circuit by drawing a simple water well and pipe on the chalkboard. Or, they can place a clear, plastic drinking straw in a glass of water. Water will not flow through the pipe (or up the straw) unless there is a pump (or force) to push it. Voltage provides that "push" for an electric circuit.

Students Acquiring English Have students work in pairs. One student can finger-trace the path of electricity from the power station to customers. The partner can describe the process.

 Students should indicate that the power near the transformer plant (230,000 v) is about 19 times as great as the power at the substation (12,000 v).

3. Assess Understanding

Provide clean, empty, cardboard milk cartons, heavy yarn, and thin string. Challenge small groups of students to construct a model showing how electric power leaves a power station and travels through transmission lines and then transformers before it reaches their homes or school.

Reading Focus Answer

A generator in a power plant produces electricity that travels to a transformer, where the voltage is increased. Electricity then travels long distances over heavy-duty power lines to transformers at a substation that reduces the voltage. From the substation, electricity travels to a transformer at a power pole, where the voltage is decreased, and then to homes and other buildings.

Electricity From Sunlight

Reading Focus Point out that students will need to *draw conclusions* from the text and graphics to answer the Reading Focus question.

1. Get Ready

Vocabulary
Science Terms solar energy, solar cell
Support Terms solar calculator, fossil fuels

2. Guide the Discussion

Connecting to the Activities
- *A Magnetic Source, p. D57*
- **What disadvantages might there be to relying on solar collectors for generating electricity?** Little or no electricity would be generated at night or on days when the Sun didn't shine.

 Meeting Individual Needs

Inclusion Challenge students to identify the solar cell on a solar-powered calculator. Encourage them to find out what happens when they cover the solar cell.

3. Assess Understanding

Pairs of students can make two word webs, with solar energy as the central concept. One web should include the advantages, the other the disadvantages. Have students use Activity Support Master "Web" (TRB p. 15).

Reading Focus Answer

A solar cell is a device that changes light into electrical energy. A solar cell is powered by the energy of the Sun. A solar panel, which consists of many solar cells, can produce electrical energy for devices such as cars and toys and even for homes.

Electricity From Sunlight

Reading Focus What is a solar cell, and how is it used in a solar panel?

 Did you ever use a solar calculator? **Solar energy,** or the energy of the Sun, powers the calculator. Inside solar calculators are solar cells. A **solar cell** is a device that changes light into electrical energy. Solar cells are so sensitive they even work on overcast days.

Solar Cells, Clean Energy
About 25 power plants in the United States use solar cells to produce electricity. Solar cells produce electricity in a way that helps keep the environment clean. Burning coal or oil to produce electricity can pollute the air. Using nuclear energy can create toxic wastes that pollute water and land.

Another advantage of using solar energy is that it helps to save fossil fuels. The amount of solar energy Earth receives in 12 hours is equal to the energy produced from burning fossil fuels in one year! Look at the photographs to see some uses of solar cells.

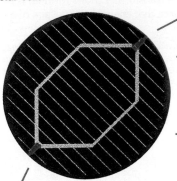

▲ One solar cell produces a tiny amount of electricity. Because of this, many cells are connected in panels.

Solar-powered airplane ▼

D64

Science & the Arts

DRAW DESIGNS
What to Do Students could create designs for futuristic solar-powered devices, including appliances, vehicles, sports equipment, clothing, and jewelry. Encourage them to use color, shape, and texture to make the designs appealing.
What's the Result? Display the designs and allow students to describe how they came up with their idea and why they think it may be a desirable product. **What are the benefits and problems of using solar power for your design?** Benefits may include less bulk than batteries; problems may include that the device can only be used in the daytime.
Multi-Age Classroom Students could work in small design teams to brainstorm and then decide on and produce a final design.

▲ Solar-powered car

◄ Solar-powered watch

▲ Solar-powered toy

Solar-powered home ►

INVESTIGATION 1 WRAP-UP

REVIEW

1. What energy change takes place in a generator? in a dry cell? in a solar cell?

2. Compare how electricity is produced by a generator with how it's produced by an electric cell.

CRITICAL THINKING

3. List and discuss at least two advantages of using solar energy over energy from burning fossil fuels.

4. Certain electric devices, such as cordless telephones, have small transformers that plug into a wall. What do the transformers do?

D65

Assessment

Performance

Role-playing Students can role-play a feature news report on how electricity is generated and brought to homes. One student might take the part of the reporter, one the part of a consumer, and one an electric company representative.

Investigation Review ►

Use Investigation Review p. 128 in the *Teacher Resource Book*.

Investigation Review

Circle the word or words that best complete each sentence.

1. A device that uses a wire coil and a magnet to produce electricity is a (generator, battery).

2. In an electric cell, energy stored in (magnets, chemicals) changes to electrical energy.

3. The force that pushes electricity along wires is (charge, voltage).

4. A (transformer, generator) changes the voltage of a current.

5. Solar cells change (chemical energy, sunlight) to electrical energy.

 A

6. Study the picture of an electricity experiment. Write O for each sentence that shows an observation. Write I for each sentence that shows an inference.

  I No current is flowing in pictures A and C.

  O The magnet is moving inside the cardboard tube in picture B.

  I A current is flowing through the wire in picture B.

  I The cause of the needle's movement in picture B is an electric current.

  O In picture C the magnet stops moving and so does the needle.

B

C

Process Skills Accept all reasonable answers.
Making a Hypothesis Responses should indicate that

If you were going on a remote camping trip, which kind of items would you pack in your suitcase—items powered by electrical energy that comes from chemical energy or items that plug into a circuit? Why? Provide examples to illustrate your answer. Write your answer on a separate sheet of paper.

items powered by chemical energy (batteries) are preferable for camping because electrical outlets might not be available.

Close
the Investigation

INVESTIGATION WRAP-UP

REVIEW

1. Electricity is produced in all three devices. In a generator, energy of motion is changed to electrical energy. In a battery, chemical energy is changed into electrical energy. In a solar cell, solar energy is changed into electrical energy.

2. A generator changes energy of motion into electrical energy; an electric cell changes chemical energy into electrical energy.

CRITICAL THINKING

3. Accept all reasonable answers. Responses might include that using solar energy not only helps save fossil fuels, but produces less pollution than using energy from burning fossil fuels.
(Applying, Synthesizing)

4. They change the voltage of the house current to a lower voltage for running the device.
(Analyzing, Synthesizing, Applying)

CHALLENGE

Tell students that the voltage of batteries they have used at home is in the range of 1.5 volts to 9 volts. Ask why a transformer has to be part of the adapter that can be plugged into a wall outlet to power a battery-operated toy. Explanations should include that the voltage in the outlet is 120 volts and the transformer must lower the voltage.

FOLLOWING UP

Baseline Assessment Return to the word web students made at the beginning of the investigation. Have them add or delete items as they wish.

Reteaching Give groups of students a battery, magnet, wire coil, string, pictures of waterfalls, power plants, homes, and schools. Ask them to choose the items they would use to make a model of how electricity is generated at a power plant and then delivered to a home or school. Have them work in pairs or small groups to build the models. Provide assistance as needed.

Use *Science Notebook*, TRB p. 70.

Start
the Investigation

How Is Electricity Useful?
pages D66–D76

Planner

Subconcept Electric current is changed into useful forms of energy in electric devices.

Objectives

- **Make** and **use a model** electromagnet.
- **Evaluate** the impact of electricity, magnetism, electromagnets, and the devices they make possible.

Pacing 3–4 class periods

Science Term electromagnet

Activate
Prior Knowledge

Baseline Assessment Ask: **About how many times a day do you depend on electricity or electric devices?** Name five of these devices. Make a list of students' estimates and appliances and save them for use in Following Up at the end of the investigation.

How Is Electricity Useful?

Light and sound come from your TV. Heat comes from your toaster oven. A motor spins inside your toy car. In all these examples, electricity is changed into another form of energy to make it useful. Explore some of these energy changes and how to stay safe around electricity.

Activity

Make It Move

How can you use electricity to make something move? Find out in this activity.

MATERIALS
- insulated wire (stripped on ends, 125 cm)
- metric ruler
- iron nail
- 10 paper clips
- dry cell (size D) in holder
- *Science Notebook*

Procedure

1. **Measure** about 20 cm from one end of a 125-cm length of insulated wire. From that point, wrap 25 turns of the wire around a nail. You will have a length of free wire at both ends of the nail, as shown.

See **SCIENCE and MATH TOOLBOX** page H6 if you need to review **Using a Tape Measure or Ruler.**

Step 1

D66

Activity Make It Move

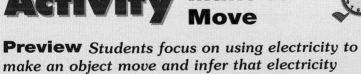

Preview *Students focus on using electricity to make an object move and infer that electricity can make some objects act like magnets.*

Advance Preparation *See p. D54b.*

1. Get Ready

 GROUPS OF 4–6   **30 MINUTES**

Key Science Process Skills measure, predict, control variables, define operationally

Materials Hints The paper clips must be metal; the nail must be made of iron or steel.

Meeting Individual Needs

STUDENTS ACQUIRING ENGLISH

Provide groups of students with sheets of drawing paper. Students can draw each circuit in the activity on a separate sheet of paper: the circuit from steps 1 and 2, the circuit from steps 3 and 4, and finally the circuit from steps 5 and 6. Remind them that each drawing needs to be properly labeled, that each should show the battery, wire connections (or not), the wire coil (including the number of turns), the nail, and the number of paper clips the nail picked up. Have them circle the variable that changed in each of the drawings. Be sure to check student predictions before they set up each trial.

VISUAL/SPATIAL

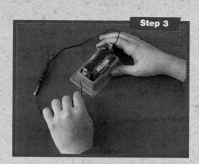
Step 3

2. Make a small pile of paper clips. **Talk with your group** and together **predict** whether bringing the nail close to the paper clips will have any effect on the paper clips. **Record** your prediction in your *Science Notebook*. **Test** your prediction and **record** your observations.

3. Attach each end of the wire to a different end of a dry cell, as shown.

4. **Predict** what will happen if you now bring the tip of the nail toward the paper clips. **Record** your prediction. **Test** your prediction and **record** your observations.

5. Disconnect the wire ends from the dry cell. Again bring the nail close to the paper clips. **Record** your observations.

6. Wrap 25 more turns of wire around the nail. Leave the nail bare at the end. Repeat steps 3 and 4.

Analyze and Conclude

1. **Compare** your predictions about the nail and the paper clips with your observations.

2. A magnet made when an electric current is sent through a wire wrapped around iron is an **electromagnet** (ē lek′trō mag nit). How does adding more turns of wire affect an electromagnet? Give evidence to support your inference.

3. What happens to an electromagnet when the current is turned off? What can you **infer** about electromagnets?

UNIT PROJECT LINK

Have you seen electric devices that run on solar cells, such as solar toys or solar hats with propellers? Ask your teacher for a solar cell. Work with your group to design a solar-powered machine. Display your invention.

 Technology Link

For more help with your Unit Project, go to **www.eduplace.com**.

D67

UNIT PROJECT LINK

Before groups of students begin designing their solar-powered machine, suggest they discuss the best location on the machine to place the solar cells in order to receive the Sun's light. Encourage students to write down their ideas for machines on *Science Notebook,* TRB, p. 73. Then they can use Unit Project Master 4 (TRB p. 20) for ideas on machines they can design.

TechnologyLink

Visit **www.eduplace.com** for a scoring rubric to assess students' progress and to share students' results on-line.

---

2. Guide the Procedure

- For best results, make sure students have the coil-and-nail assembly completed and the paper clips in place before they attach the wires to the battery terminals.
- Have students recall what they have learned about magnets. Ask: **When the nail is connected to the battery, is it a permanent or temporary magnet?** It is a temporary magnet. When the wires are disconnected from the battery, the nail loses its magnetism.
- **Would a current flow if both ends of the wire were attached to the same terminal? Why or why not?** No, the described setup is an incomplete circuit.

 Have students record their predictions and observations and answers to the questions on *Science Notebook,* TRB, pp. 71–72.

 Science Processor You might wish to have students use the CD-ROM Spreadsheet to organize and display their data.

3. Assess Performance

Process Skills Checklist

- Did students accurately **measure** the wire lengths?
- Did students **identify** electric current and the number of turns in the wire as **variables**?
- Did students accurately **predict** the relationship between a nail and paper clips and the number of turns in the coil and the strength of the magnet?
- Did students **infer** that an electromagnet's strength increases as more coils are added?

Analyze and Conclude

1. During the first step, most students probably predicted, accurately, that the nail would have no effect on the paper clips.

2. Students should infer that more coils in the wire will result in a stronger magnet. To support this inference, students should cite their observations that a nail with a greater number of turns in the wire can pick up a greater number of paper clips.

3. When the current is off, the nail is not magnetic. Students should infer that the nail acts as a magnet because (and only when) an electric current travels through the coil around the nail.

Long Distance, Short Time

1. Get Ready

Vocabulary

Support Term telecommunication

Background

- In the 150 years since the invention of the telegraph, the science of communication has grown and within the last ten years it has exploded. Each advancement was a refinement and improvement on existing technology. The ease of communications has allowed people around the world to share information at the speed of light. One result is that often, many researchers at many different locations can work in concert toward the same goal. The following are a few of the early landmarks made in the field of communications.

1830s—Samuel F. B. Morse and Alfred Vail (United States) patented the electric telegraph.

1895—Guglielmo Marconi (Italy) devised a telegraph without wires.

1897—Karl Ferdinand Braun (Germany) invented a tube that helped lead to the development of television.

1926—John Logie Baird (Scotland) transmitted the first picture of a human face over television.

Discussion Starter

- **How could you tell your cousins in Hong Kong that you got a puppy for your birthday?** Students' responses might include a telephone call, a letter, a card, a videotape sent by mail, or an E-mail message.

- **What's the fastest way to tell your cousins and show them a picture of you and your new puppy?** Students may have many suggestions. Reinforce any answers that rely on computer images, E-mail, telephone/television images, and so on.

Long Distance, Short Time

Reading Focus What types of devices help us communicate with one another?

 How do you communicate (kə myōō'ni kāt) with friends over long distances? Do you talk on the phone? Do you use electronic mail, or E-mail, on a computer? If so, then you use telecommunication (tel i-kə myōō ni kā'shən). This is using electricity for almost instant communication over a long distance.

Electricity has made telecommunication possible, beginning with the invention of the telegraph. Today people link television, telephones, and computers all over the world. These devices work together in a system that provides information, communication, and entertainment. The time line shows some highlights in the field of telecommunication since the 1840s.

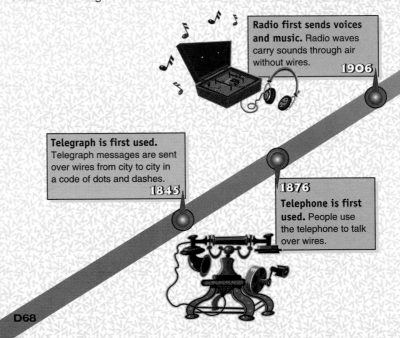

Radio first sends voices and music. Radio waves carry sounds through air without wires. **1906**

Telegraph is first used. Telegraph messages are sent over wires from city to city in a code of dots and dashes. **1845**

1876 Telephone is first used. People use the telephone to talk over wires.

D68

Integrating the Sciences

 LIFE SCIENCE

What to Do Encourage students to discuss why communication is important to animals. (The reasons may be different for different species.) Then have students research and report on the ways different kinds of animals send and receive messages.

What's the Result? The class can construct a chart comparing the ways different animals communicate. **What are some ways animals make sounds?** Answers may include vibrating vocal cords, tapping beaks on trees, vibrating wings, and vibrating membranes in the abdomen. **What are some ways animals hear sounds?** Some examples are through large ears on their heads, ears on their sides, ears at the base of their wings, and ears on their legs.

Internet system is in use.
People use the Internet to send information from computer to computer. They use this system to communicate almost instantly throughout the world.
1990s

Communications satellite *Telestar* is sent into space.
Satellites carry live television, radio, telephone calls, and computer data all over the world.
1962

2000
Video phones are used.
Users can see the person they're talking to on a video screen.

1980s
Cellular (sel'yōō lər) **phones and fax machines are in use.** Cellular phones allow people to talk on the phone as they travel. Facsimile (fak sim'ə lē), also called fax, machines are used to send written messages over telephone lines.

1936
Television programs are broadcast.
Television sends clear pictures and sound.

INVESTIGATE FURTHER!

RESEARCH

Analyze television commercials for three phone companies. Infer and then determine which company would save you the most money if you talked to a friend in another state for 17 minutes.

D69

INVESTIGATE FURTHER!

RESEARCH

Remind students that the cost of the telephone call may include more than the cents/minute fee. Encourage students to find out if low per minute rates are tied to monthly fees, monthly minimums, or some other additional charge. Tell students to record their finding on *Science Notebook,* TRB, p. 74.

 Science Processor You may wish to suggest that students use the CD-ROM Spreadsheet to organize and display their data.

---

2. Guide the Discussion

Choose from the following strategies to facilitate discussion.

Thinking About the Data
• **How can the latest developments in the field of telecommunication change how you do your homework?** Responses should address the ability of a student to access an extensive variety of information from a single computer terminal hooked up to a telephone.

Drawing Conclusions
• **Do you think that fax machines would exist today if telephones had not been invented?** Students will probably conclude that fax machines would not exist today since fax messages travel over telephone lines. **How might the absence of fax machines affect people's lives?** Students' responses will probably relate to the speed at which fax machines transmit information.

Meeting Individual Needs
For Extra Help Copy each of the events listed on this time line onto separate index cards, omitting the date from each. Mix the cards and allow pairs of students to correctly sequence the events.

3. Assess Understanding

Student groups can work together to prepare bulletin board displays of pictures and/or drawings of old and new communications devices such as TVs, radios, stereo components, telephones, and computers. Discuss changes in size—the latest devices such as computers and radios are generally smaller and more compact than their predecessors.

Reading Focus Answer

Devices that help people communicate with one another include radios, telephones, video phones, cellular phones, fax machines, computers, television, and satellites.

Electric Magnets

Reading Focus Have students *preview* the resource to *predict* which section may provide information to answer the Reading Focus question. Then have them read to *confirm their predictions*.

1. Get Ready

Vocabulary
Science Term electromagnet
Support Terms recycling, motors

Discussion Starter
• **What do a battery-operated clock, a clothes dryer, a battery-operated toy car, and an electric mixer have in common?** Allow students to offer all possibilities they can. Then point out that all of these devices use electric current to produce motion.

• Ask: **What word parts can you find in the word** *electromagnet?* **What clue do these word parts give you about the meaning of the term** *electromagnet?* Students should recognize that the components of the term *electromagnet* include the word *magnet* and the word part *electro-*, which is very similar to *electric*.

Electric Magnets

Reading Focus What are some uses of electromagnets?

Did you ever flip a coin? When the heads side of the coin is up, you can't see the tails side. But you know the tails side is there. In a way, electricity and magnetism are like the two sides of a coin.

In Investigation 1 you found one way that magnetism and electricity are related. Moving a coil of wire in a magnetic field produces electric current. In this way, magnetism produces electricity.

Electricity and magnetism are also related in another way. In the activity on pages D66 and D67, a dry cell and a nail are used to make an electromagnet. An **electromagnet** is a magnet made when electric charges move through a coil of wire wrapped around an iron core, or center. In an electromagnet, electricity is used to produce magnetism.

Properties of Electromagnets

Electromagnets are like natural magnets in some ways. Like natural magnets, they attract materials that contain iron. Electromagnets have a north pole and a south pole. An electromagnet also has a magnetic field, as the drawing above shows.

This electromagnet makes it easy to separate steel from other materials. The magnet is turned on in order to lift the steel. ▶

D70

Science & Social Studies

ELECTRIC INVENTOR
What You Need tape recorder, cassette, magnet
What to Do Explain that African-American James E. West is a coinventor of foil electrets, which are like permanent magnets. Electrets convert sound into electrical signals that can be heard in telephones, tape recorders, hearing aids, and small microphones. West's research focused on the electromagnetism within the foil. Students can test the effects of a magnet on a tape in the following way. They can tape their voices, play the tape, remove the tape from the player, move a magnet over the tape, and play it again.
What's the Result? **What happened?** The sound was erased because the magnet changed the magnetic pattern on the tape.

How are electromagnets different from other magnets? In Chapter 1, a temporary magnet is made by stroking a nail with a bar magnet. Recall that a temporary magnet slowly loses its magnetism over time. An electromagnet is a different kind of temporary magnet. It acts like a magnet only while electric current flows through it. As soon as you turn off the current, it loses its magnetism. As a result, an electromagnet can be turned on or off.

Using Electromagnets

Imagine that you're in charge of a collection center for recycling. People dump bags of cans made of different metals in one big pile. But the cans made of steel and those made of aluminum have to be sent to different places to be recycled. This means that you have to separate the two kinds of cans. One way to do this job is by using a large electromagnet, as the pictures below show.

After the crane swings away from the pile of mixed materials, the magnet is turned off. Then the steel objects fall into a separate pile. ▶

D71

Integrating the Sciences

EARTH SCIENCE

What You Need electromagnet used in the activity "Make It Move," p. D66; variety of small metal and nonmetal items such as bottle caps, paper clips, paper scraps, cloth scraps, and so on.

What to Do Students can use the electromagnet to simulate what occurs in a recycling collection center. First they should scramble the materials to form small piles and then try to separate the steel materials from the others. Next they should reassemble the piles and use the electromagnet to see which materials it attracts.

What's the Result? How does using an electromagnet benefit recycling? It speeds up the process of separating discarded materials for recycling, which makes it less costly to recycle.

2. Guide the Discussion

Choose from the following strategies to facilitate discussion.

Connecting to the Activities

• *Make It Move, p. D68*
• **What materials would you need to show that electricity can produce magnetism and that magnetism can produce electricity?** Students should list the materials from Make It Move as well as the bar magnet from A Magnetic Source in Investigation 1.

Identifying and Solving Problems

• **What materials could you use to make a magnetic door latch that you could open without touching the door? What kind of magnet would you need? Explain your answer.** The latch needs to have an electromagnet. With this device, a person can operate a switch to turn the magnet "off" whenever he or she wants to open the door.

Meeting Individual Needs

Gifted and Talented Explain to students that an electric motor works because a current flows across a magnetic field. Provide a small electric motor such as the ones in hair dryers or small fans. Under supervision, allow students to take the motor apart. Then have them draw each part. Students should label their drawings with the name and function of each part.

Thinking Critically

- **Do electromagnets have north and south poles? How could you design an experiment to find out?** Students can use the compass, without the wire coil around it from the Detect a Current activity, to see if the electromagnet has poles.

- **Think about each room in your home. In your mind, list the items in each room that use electromagnets. Which of these items do you think you and your family could live without? Which are necessities?** Responses will vary with the items listed and students' opinions regarding "necessities" and "luxuries." For example, some students might list doorbells and hair dryers as electromagnetic "luxuries," but the telephone and VCR as "necessities."

Science in Literature

Hello! Hello! A Look Inside the Telephone by Eve and Albert Stwertka

Students can find an explanation of how a telephone works on pp. 15–23. Have students work with a partner to explain how the two magnets work together to create their voice on a telephone receiver.

3. Assess Understanding

Have students work together to draw an electromagnet that uses a wire, a battery, and a nail. Then have them draw two more magnets, each more powerful than the first.

Reading Focus Answer

The uses of electromagnets include the following: in cranes to separate steel from aluminum, in loudspeakers, telephones, VCRs, cassette players, doorbells, and in electric motors in devices such as refrigerators, clocks, hair dryers, vacuum cleaners, and ceiling fans.

When you push a doorbell, a circuit closes and the electromagnet pulls on the hammer, which strikes the bell. ▶

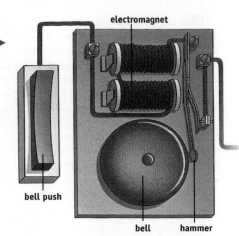

Many objects in your home have electromagnets in them. These electromagnets are hidden inside loudspeakers, telephones, VCRs, cassette players, and doorbells. All electric motors contain electromagnets, too. Electric motors run refrigerators, clocks, hair dryers, vacuum cleaners, and ceiling fans.

Take another look at the pictures on page D40 in Chapter 2. Electric motors drive many of the devices shown there, too. What other things can you think of that are run by electric motors? ■

Science in Literature

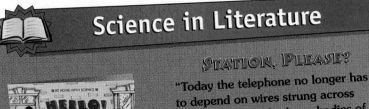

**Hello! Hello!
A Look Inside the Telephone**
by Eve and Albert Stwertka
Illustrated by Mena Dolobowsky
Julian Messner, 1991

STATION, PLEASE?

"Today the telephone no longer has to depend on wires strung across mountains or under large bodies of water. Because sound waves can now be changed into radio signals, part of the wire circuit can be replaced by radio."

This quotation from *Hello! Hello! A Look Inside the Telephone* by Eve and Albert Stwertka helps you realize how phones have changed communication. Read this book to find out how the first telephones were different from the one you may have today.

D72

Science & Math

ESTIMATING

What to Do Remind students that all motors contain electromagnets. Then have students estimate the number of electromagnets that can be found at home. Have them go on a hunt in their home to find devices with electromagnets such as a hair dryer, doorbell, cassette player, CD player, power drill, VCR, telephone, refrigerator, washer, clothes dryer, camcorder, computer, and so on. Have them chart the kinds of devices found and the number of each.

What's the Result? Display students' charts in the classroom. **Were you surprised at the number of devices in your home with electromagnets? Why or why not?** Most likely, students didn't realize the number of devices with electromagnets in their homes.

A Car That Plugs In

Reading Focus What are some advantages and disadvantages of using electric cars?

Do you live in or near a large city? In many cities, air pollution is a serious problem. As you read in Chapter 1, cars that run on gasoline pollute the air. Many cars crowded together can make the air unhealthy. Using electric cars may be one way to solve this problem. These cars run on batteries, which results in less pollution.

Have you ever used a rechargeable battery? Electric cars have rechargeable batteries. As you know, batteries are made up of electric cells. The cells in the batteries of electric cars lose energy, or run down, and stop working after being used a certain length of time. When the batteries run down, they have to be recharged.

Electric cars aren't used much today. Their batteries must be recharged about once every 96 km (60 mi). Their top speed is about 80 km/h (50 mph). And electric cars cost more to operate than most gas-powered cars.

In the future, many people may drive cars that won't rely only on gasoline. Why? Gasoline is made from oil, and the need to conserve oil is great. The need to clean up the air is just as important.

Internet Field Trip
Visit **www.eduplace.com** to find out more about electric cars.

Suppose you traveled 8 km to school each day in an electric car. The car can travel 96 km (60 mi) on one charge of its batteries. How many trips could you make to school on one charge?

D73

Science, Technology & Society

ELECTRIC CARS

What to Do Students can ask a librarian to help them find articles on the development of electric-powered vehicles. Have students find out what organizations are building the cars, how many are sold, who is buying them, and how they are being used.

What's the Result? Have teams of students debate whether the government should provide money to help companies develop electric cars or to encourage the sale of electric cars.

A Car That Plugs In

Reading Focus Encourage students to use their *prior knowledge* to *predict* some advantages and disadvantages of electric cars. Have them read to *confirm their predictions*.

1. Get Ready

Vocabulary

Support Terms air pollution, rechargeable battery

2. Guide the Discussion

Identifying and Solving Problems

- **The batteries in electric cars need to be recharged about every 60 miles. How would this change the way we live or drive?** Trips would have to be planned around frequent recharging stops; the charge in the battery would need to be carefully monitored in cases of frequent short trips.

Students should indicate that they can make 96 km ÷ 8 km/trip = 12 trips.

3. Assess Understanding

Have students work in small groups to design and draw battery-operated cars. Then have each group write a jingle advertising the car's advantages.

Reading Focus Answer

The advantages of using electric cars over other cars are that they produce less air pollution and that their use helps to conserve oil. The disadvantages over other cars are that they are not as fast, that they cost more to operate, and that the batteries that run them need recharging.

Internet Field Trip

From **www.eduplace.com** students can link to a Web site about electric cars. A trip log will guide their visit to the site.

Safety Around Electricity

Reading Focus Ask students what they can *conclude* about electricity based on the Reading Focus question. If needed, focus attention on the word *safe.* Have them read and use the graphics to check their conclusions.

1. Get Ready

Vocabulary
Support Terms voltage, short circuit, power failure, fuse, circuit breaker

Background
• William H. Merrill, an engineer, wanted to test light bulbs he suspected caused fires. In 1894, he founded Underwriters' Laboratories, Inc. (UL), a company that attempts to classify and determine the safety of various materials and products. Eventually the company expanded to serve manufacturers and others interested in safety tests.

Discussion Starter
• Display a variety of Danger High Voltage, Caution, Electrical Hazard, Stand Clear—Electrocution Hazard, and Caution—Electric Fence signs. These signs, or copies of these signs, are available from local power companies and fire protection agencies. Ask: **Where would you expect to see these signs? What do these signs mean?** Students may easily identify these signs and their meanings. However, stress that these signs generally occur near industrial areas, where children should not play.

2. Guide the Discussion

Connecting to the Activities
• *Make It Move, p. D66*
• Have students examine the dry cells they used in the activity. Ask them to identify the voltage of each and compare these values to the voltage (at least 110 volts) used in their homes. Students should compute that residential voltages are nearly 75 times that of the 1.5-volt dry cells used in the activity.

Safety Around Electricity

Reading Focus What are some ways to be safe around electricity?

In the activities, electric current is sent through wires. But why are those wires safe to touch? The activities use size D dry cells that are marked 1.5 v, which stands for 1.5 volts. A current with such a low voltage has very little energy. But the voltage of the current in the wiring of a house is 110 volts or more. This electric current is dangerous. But you can be safe if you follow certain safety rules.

DON'T use any appliance that has a torn cord or a cord that is worn out. If two bare wires of a cord touch each other while the cord is in use, current will go to the crossed wires and back to its source. This is an example of a short circuit. In a short circuit, wires overheat. Overheated wires can cause a fire. ▶

◀ **NEVER** stick your finger or anything else except an electrical plug into an electrical outlet. Be sure any electrical plug you use is in good condition. Also, always hold a cord by its plug when you pull it from an outlet. What do you think is the reason for this rule?

D74

Science & the Arts

DESIGN SIGNS
What You Need art supplies such as colored pencils, paints, glue, scissors, posterboard
What to Do Students can design international warning signs, using symbols and no words, or posters for two of the situations shown.
What's the Result? Arrange for students to display their signs and posters for the entire school. Also, if they feel comfortable doing so, encourage your bilingual students to explain the posters to others who speak the same language.
Multi-Age Classroom Students could work in small groups to think of ideas for their warning signs. Each group member should be encouraged to suggest an idea.

DON'T overload circuits. Plugging too many appliances into one circuit can overload the circuit. Wires in overloaded circuits can become hot enough to start fires. ▶

◀ **STAY AWAY** from anything with a sign that says "High Voltage." Voltages in electric power lines and electric rails are even higher, and more dangerous, than they are in house current.

DANGER
HIGH VOLTAGE

NEVER touch an electrical cord, appliance, or light switch when you are wet. Unless water is pure, it is a conductor. Electric current can pass through the water and your body more easily than through an appliance. Any water that's in contact with a person's body is not pure. ▶

D75

Science & Social Studies

SAFETY FIRST

What You Need book on first aid and/or safety procedures, posterboard, markers

What to Do Share with students the story of African-American Dr. Raphael Lee, a scientist researching ways to help people who have suffered electrical burns recover. Explain that electrical burns affect the body differently than do thermal, or heat, burns. Encourage pairs or small groups of students to research safety information on how to help a person who has suffered an electrical burn. Students can make posters illustrating some of the safety tips.

What's the Result? Display posters in the classroom. Discuss some of the safety tips for assisting electrical burn victims.

Transparency 21: Visual/Spatial Activity
Use the transparency "Using Electricity Safely" to reinforce students' understanding of electrical safety rules.

Thinking Critically
- **A power line has fallen from a utility pole. Why is it not safe to touch the power line?** Your hand and body could complete a circuit allowing the electricity to move from the power line through your body, causing injury.

Making Inferences
- **Why should you remove a plug from a wall socket by holding the plug rather than the cord?** Pulling on the cord could loosen the connection between the cord and the plug, leading to a short circuit and possibly a fire.

Making Comparisons
- **Why are you required to get out of a public swimming pool if thunder is heard?** Thunder and lightning occur together. It can be very dangerous to be in or near bodies of water when lightning strikes.

Meeting Individual Needs
Students Acquiring English Make pairs of flash cards for each of the situations shown on pp. D74–D75. Include both a dangerous practice and the correct way to react to the electrical hazard. Show the pairs to students and make sure they are able to choose the safe alternative in each pair.

3. Assess Understanding

Pairs of students can work together to present a pantomime of the "do's" and "don'ts" of electricity. One student can pantomime the action while the other student supplies the narrative.

Reading Focus Answer

Ways to be safe around electricity include not using cords that are worn, never sticking your finger or anything else except an electrical plug into an electrical outlet, taking care to hold a cord by its plug when you pull it from an outlet, not overloading a circuit, staying away from power lines with high voltage, and never touching an electrical cord, appliance, or light switch when you are wet.

Close
the Investigation

INVESTIGATION WRAP-UP

REVIEW

1. An electromagnet is a magnet consisting of a coil of wire wrapped around an iron core; the assembly becomes a magnet when electricity flows through the wire.

2. Students' lists will vary but might include loudspeakers, telephones, VCRs, cassette players, clocks, hair dryers, refrigerators, vacuum cleaners, ceiling fans, and doorbells.

CRITICAL THINKING

3. A car that used both electricity and gasoline would use less gasoline—this would help conserve oil and help clean air pollution. A combination car might be able to travel farther and faster between charges than an all-electric car. *(Analyzing, Synthesizing, Evaluating)*

4. Battery-operated radios will not electrocute you if they come in contact with water because they operate on a much lower voltage than radios you plug into house current. *(Applying, Expressing Ideas)*

CHALLENGE

Suggest students live without electricity for two hours on a designated day. Have them list what tasks or activities they had to change in order to successfully meet the challenge.

FOLLOWING UP

Baseline Assessment Review with students their lists of estimates and appliances they made at the beginning of the investigation. Ask them if they would like to change their time estimates. Also allow them the opportunity to add devices to their lists.

Reteaching Have pairs of students use the Activity Support Master "Web" on TRB p. 15 to make word webs with Electricity as the main topic. Have students incorporate into the map the concept of electromagnetism, the hazards of electricity, and things made possible due to this flow of electrons. Pairs of students can work with one or two other groups to review the maps.

 Use *Science Notebook,* TRB p. 75.

Have you ever had a power failure in your home? This can happen if a fuse blows or a circuit breaker switches off. As you read in Chapter 2, page D52, fuses and circuit breakers are safety devices. They open circuits when wires get too hot.

What should be done when a fuse blows or a circuit breaker trips, or switches off? First, it's important to find out the cause. Is there an overloaded circuit? Is there a short circuit somewhere? The cause of the overheating should be corrected. Then an adult in your home should replace the fuse or turn the circuit breaker back on. ■

▲ A home circuit-breaker box

▲ A good fuse

▲ A blown fuse

INVESTIGATION 2 WRAP-UP

REVIEW

1. What is an electromagnet?

2. List at least six devices that contain electromagnets.

CRITICAL THINKING

3. What are some advantages of an electric-gasoline combination car? What might the disadvantages be?

4. How would you explain to a group of first graders why radios used in a bathroom should be battery-powered?

D76

Assessment

Investigation Review

Use the words in the box to complete each sentence.

electric	overloaded	electromagnet
batteries	fuses	

1. Electric cars do not pollute the air because they run on __batteries__.

2. Household appliances, such as refrigerators and vacuum cleaners, have __electric__ motors.

3. When a coil of wire is wrapped around a nail and attached to a dry cell, the nail can become a(n) __electromagnet__.

4. A(n) __overloaded__ circuit is always a safety hazard because wires can become very hot, which could cause a fire.

5. __Fuses__ open circuits when wires get too hot.

6. Describe an electromagnet.
__An electromagnet is a magnet made when an electric__
__current passes through a wire coiled around an iron core.__
__The magnetic force of an electromagnet can be strong__
__enough to lift heavy objects that contain iron. Its__
magnetism can be turned on and off.

Process Skills
Communicating
What kinds of objects in your home or school contain electromagnets? Write your answer on a separate sheet of paper.   Answers might include loudspeakers, telephones, VCRs, tape decks, and doorbells.

Portfolio

Write a Slogan Students can work in groups of three or four to create a series of safety slogans to promote safe use of electrical equipment in school.

◄ **Investigation Review**
Use Investigation Review p. 129 in the *Teacher Resource Book.*

Word Power

Write the letter of the term that best matches the definition. *Not all terms will be used.*

1. A device that uses a wire coil and a magnet to produce electricity
2. A device that produces electric current from energy stored in chemicals
3. A device that changes sunlight into electrical energy
4. A magnet made from a wire wrapped around iron
5. The force that pushes electricity through wires

a. electrical cell
b. electromagnet
c. generator
d. solar cell
e. solar energy
f. voltage

Check What You Know

Write the word in each pair that best completes each sentence.

1. Solar energy is changed to electricity by (an electric cell, a solar cell).
2. When wires get too hot, circuit breakers (close, open) circuits.
3. Doorbells and telephones contain (generators, electromagnets).
4. Electric current can be produced by a (generator, transformer).

Problem Solving

1. A magnet passing through a coil of wire does not produce enough electric current to light a bulb. What are two ways to increase the amount of current?

2. How do you think the energy of the Sun might be used to power a motorcycle?

Study the photograph. Name the device shown and describe how it works. Explain how the usefulness of the device would change if it could not be turned on and off.

D77

Assessment

Word Power

1. c   **2.** a   **3.** d   **4.** b   **5.** f

Check What You Know

1. a solar cell   2. open
3. electromagnets   4. generator

Problem Solving

1. You could increase the amount of current by using a stronger magnet or adding coils of wire.

2. Students might suggest using a battery that is charged with energy collected by solar panels.

The device is an electromagnet, which acts as a magnet as long as electric current is flowing through it. If an electromagnet could not be turned on and off, it could not easily drop its load.

Assess Performance

Student Task

Challenge students to design an experiment that tests how changing the thickness of the iron core of an electromagnet might affect the magnet's strength. Students can use the materials from the activity on pages D66–D67.

Scoring Rubric

Points	What To Look For
3	Student has developed a clear experimental plan to show how the thickness of an iron core might affect the strength of an electromagnet.
2	Student's plan is generally logical, but some aspects are not stated clearly.
1	Student's plan is unclear, illogical and does not test the concept.

Chapter Test

Check What You Know Each item is worth 15 points.

1. What will you have to do to close the circuit below? Show your answer on the drawing.

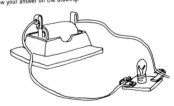

For questions 2–5, circle the letter of the correct answer.

2. Before Myra plugged in the cord of her study lamp, she noticed that the insulation on the cord was worn out. What should she do?

a. Plug in the cord, since she'll only be using the lamp for a short time.
b. Not plug in the cord until it's repaired, or buy a new lamp.
c. Be sure she holds the plug when pulling it from the outlet.
d. Plug the cord into an outlet with a number of other cords plugged into it.

Problem Solving Each item is worth 15 points.

3. Which of the following comparisons can you use to best explain voltage?

a. fire in a fireplace
b. a compass needle
c. lemon juice in a glass
d. water in a garden hose

Chapter Test

4. Juanita is a volunteer at a recycling center. Her job is to separate steel cans from aluminum cans. What device might make her job easier?

a. generator
b. current detector
c. electromagnet
d. transformer

5. How is an electric current produced in a battery?

a. Chemical energy changes into electrical energy.
b. Energy of motion changes into electrical energy.
c. Electrical energy changes into chemical energy.
d. Chemical energy changes into energy of motion.

Word Power Each item is worth 5 points.

Use the words in the box to complete each sentence.

> generators   electric cells   solar cells
> electromagnets   voltage

6. __Generators__ produce most of the electricity that you use in your home and school.

7. Electricity sets up a magnetic field around __electromagnets__.

8. The force that pushes electricity along wires is __voltage__.

9. __Solar cells__ change the Sun's energy into electrical energy.

10. A battery is made up of two or more __electric cells__.

◀ **Chapter Test**
Use pp. 130–131 in the *Teacher Resource Book.*

UNIT D
Using READING SKILLS

Drawing Conclusions

Review Reading Strategies

Have students turn to *Reading to Learn* on pp. S12–S13 to review the reading strategies.

Reinforce the Reading Skill

Ask a volunteer to read the Reading Skills title on page D78 (*Drawing Conclusions*). Reinforce that a **conclusion** is an idea or opinion that a writer tries to communicate to the reader. Then have students take turns reading aloud the introductory paragraph and the tips in the notepad ("Consider these questions . . ."). Discuss how the questions apply to the example in the introduction ("The children stared out the window."). Explain that each question tells students how they can draw conclusions from the text.

Model these strategies for drawing conclusions.

- **Before Reading** Have students read the title and the first sentence in each paragraph. Ask students: **What do the title and sentences tell you?** (Thomas Edison invented the light bulb; Lewis Latimer belonged to a team of scientists headed by Thomas Edison.) Ask students: **What do you know about the invention of the light bulb?** (Accept reasonable responses.)

- **While Reading** Point out key terms in the paragraph (*team of scientists, bulb, filament*). Tell students to think about what the writer is saying about each term. Then tell students to think about what they know about each one.

- **After Reading** Students should complete the exercises. (1. d; 2. "Latimer made a greatly improved bulb. . . .") If they are having trouble, encourage students to reread each statement in Exercise 1 and ask themselves: What do the paragraphs say about this statement?

Apply the Reading Skill

Suggest that students can use these strategies to draw conclusions from Unit Resources.

Drawing Conclusions

Often writers imply, or hint at, more information than they actually state. They give clues and expect readers to figure out the rest, using what they already know. Suppose an author writes, "The children stared out the window." A reader can conclude that something interesting was happening outside—or that the children were bored by what was happening inside.

> Consider these questions as you draw conclusions.
> - What did the author write?
> - What do I know?
> - What is my conclusion?

Read the paragraphs. Then complete the exercises that follow.

> #### Invention of the Light Bulb
>
> Thomas Edison, who headed a team of scientists called the Edison Pioneers, invented the light bulb. Edison's first bulb used a filament made of scorched thread. But this bulb was costly and didn't last long.
> Lewis Latimer was a member of the Edison Pioneers. Latimer made a greatly improved bulb that used a carbon filament. This bulb cost less and lasted longer than Edison's bulb. Carbon was later replaced by tungsten, which is used in bulbs today.

1. Which statement is a conclusion you can draw from the paragraphs? Write the letter of that statement.

   a. Edison was jealous of Latimer's success.

   b. Carbon lasts longer than tungsten and costs less.

   c. People will someday invent a better way to make electric light.

   d. Edison and Latimer should share the credit for the invention of the light bulb.

2. What was the most important clue in helping you draw that conclusion?

D78

👤 Meeting Individual Needs

STUDENTS ACQUIRING ENGLISH

Draw students' attention to the hints for drawing conclusions in the notepad at the top of the page. Point out that conclusions are based on facts that the author supplies. Have students work in a group to list the facts about Edison, Latimer, and light bulbs that appear in the paragraph. Then have them tell what the facts "add up to" or suggest about each of the statements in Exercise 1. You may wish to have the groups report their conclusions to the class.

LINGUISTIC

Using MATH SKILLS

Bar Graph

The graph below shows the estimated life span, in hours, of light bulbs of different wattages.

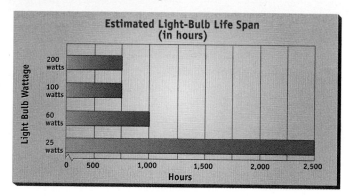

Estimated Light-Bulb Life Span (in hours)

Use the data in the graph to complete the exercises that follow.

1. Which light bulb should last the longest?

2. About how many times longer will a 25-watt light bulb last than a 60-watt bulb?

3. Which bulb, if left on continuously, will last for about one month?

4. Estimate the life span, in days, of a 60-watt light bulb.

5. Estimate the number of months a 100-watt light bulb will last if it is left on for 8 hours a day.

6. Estimate the life span, in hours, of a 150-watt light bulb. Explain your answer.

7. Estimate the life span of a 75-watt light bulb in hours. Explain your answer.

D79

Bar Graph

Reinforce the Math Skill

Be sure students understand that a bar graph is one way to organize and display data. You might wish to point out that a bar graph is particularly useful for displaying data that you wish to compare. Remind students that the bars on a bar graph can be positioned either horizontally or vertically.

Apply the Math Skill

Be sure that students read the title at the top of the bar graph as well as the labels along the left side and bottom of the graph. Once you are sure that students know how to read the graph, have them complete the pupil page.

Answers

1. 25-watt light bulb

2. About two and one half times longer.

3. Both a 100-watt bulb and a 200-watt bulb

4. Estimates will vary; about 40 days.

5. Estimates will vary; about 3 months.

6. Estimates will vary. Students may estimate about 750 hours as that is the life span of both a 100-watt bulb and a 200-watt bulb.

7. Estimates will vary. Students may estimate about 875 hours, which is between the life span of a 60-watt and a 100-watt bulb.

Science & Math

LIGHT-BULB GRAPH

What to Do The bar graph on the pupil page shows estimated light-bulb life spans in hours. Have students determine the estimated life span for each bulb in days. Have them round each number to the nearest ten and use their data to create a bar graph.

What's the Result? Check students' graphs. Remind students to include labels and a title for their graphs.

THINK LIKE A SCIENTIST

Before students begin with this page, you may want to have them review the steps in the scientific process. Refer students to pages S2–S11 and have them briefly summarize how they would apply the process as they complete the page. They can refer to their summaries as they proceed with the steps of the Unit Wrap-up.

✏️ WRITING IN SCIENCE

Have students write their instructions for another fourth grader to follow. Students can brainstorm with a partner to come up with ideas for materials and for the design of the switch.

Use these questions to evaluate student performance.

- Is the materials list complete?
- Are the instructions clearly stated?
- Are steps listed in chronological order?
- Have spelling and capitalization been checked?

UNIT PROJECT WRAP-UP

Provide a time and place for an inventor's fair at which students display their tricks, puzzles, games, and inventions that use magnetism or electricity. In addition, students can brainstorm ideas for an invention that uses both electricity and magnetism—possibly a combination or variation of the devices already developed. Students might draw detailed designs before constructing. This will help them determine what materials they may need. After completion, encourage students to propose ways of improving their invention.

- For more information on how to wrap up the Unit Project, see pages D1o and D1p.
- For suggestions on how to assess the Unit Project, see Unit Project Scoring Rubric Master 5 (Teacher Resource Book p. 21).

UNIT D WRAP-UP!

On your own, use scientific methods to investigate a question about magnetism and electricity.

THINK LIKE A SCIENTIST

Ask a Question

Pose a question about magnetism and electricity that you would like to investigate. For example, ask, "What effect does changing voltage have on an electromagnet?"

Make a Hypothesis

Suggest a hypothesis that is a possible answer to the question. One hypothesis is that increasing voltage increases the strength of an electromagnet.

Plan and Do a Test

Plan a controlled experiment to find whether or not increasing voltage increases the strength of an electromagnet. You could start with insulated wire, a metric ruler, an iron nail, paper clips, and dry cells. Develop a procedure that uses these materials to test the hypothesis. With permission, carry out your experiment. Follow the safety guidelines on pages S14–S15.

Record and Analyze

Observe carefully and record your data accurately. Make repeated observations.

Draw Conclusions

Look for evidence to support the hypothesis or to show that it is false. Draw conclusions about the hypothesis. Repeat the experiment to verify the results.

WRITING IN SCIENCE
Giving Instructions

Write a description of how to set up and operate a simple series circuit that includes a light bulb and a switch. Use these guidelines for writing your instructions.

- Keep in mind the person, or audience, who will read your instructions.
- List the materials for making the circuit.
- Write the steps in chronological order.

D80

Home-School Connection

The Closing Letter at the end of this unit suggests an additional activity using magnetism that family members can do at home. Distribute the Closing Letter (TRB p. 7) to students at the end of this unit.

Closing Letter

Dear Family,

We hope that you and your child have enjoyed finding out about magnetism and electricity. Would you like to learn more? Here is an activity that you can do together.

Magnetic Soccer

You will need

- large piece of stiff cardboard
- thin cardboard
- crayons or marking pens
- scissors
- metal thumbtacks
- modeling clay or cork
- two thin sticks
- tape
- two small magnets
- table tennis ball
- books or bricks

Build the game board

- Make a drawing of a soccer field on the stiff cardboard. Make two goals from the stiff cardboard as well. Attach them to either end of the field. Then tape strips of cardboard around the outside of the field to keep the ball from dropping off.
- Draw small pictures of soccer players on the thin cardboard. Cut out the pictures, leaving a flap at the bottom of each picture. Fold each flap under, push a thumbtack up through the flap, and put a piece of clay or cork over the sharp point of the thumbtack. Place the players and the ball randomly on the field.
- Tape a magnet to one end of each of the two thin sticks. Raise the playing field by resting it on some books or bricks so that you can slide the magnetic sticks underneath the field.

Play the game

- To play, move the magnetic sticks underneath the field, moving the players so that they hit the ball.
- See who can score the most goals. Talk about how magnetism works in this game.

TEACHER NOTES

CREDITS

Student Edition

ILLUSTRATORS

Cover Genine Smith.

Think Like a Scientist 14: Laurie Hamilton. *Border* Genine Smith.

Unit D 13: Patrick Gnan. 15: Dan McGowan. 22: Brad Gaber. 30–31: Robert Roper. 35: t. Jim Effier; m. Andrew Shiff. 40: David Winter. 41: Hans & Cassady, Inc. 42–43: Dale Gustafson. 48: Patrick Gnan. 50–51: Hans & Cassady, Inc. 52: Robert Roper. 53: Hans & Cassady, Inc. 60–61: Robert Roper. 62–63: Geoffrey McCormick. 68–69: Vincent Wayne. 70, 72: Robert Roper. 74–76: Michael Sloan.

Science and Math Toolbox *Logos* Nancy Tobin. 14–15: Andrew Shiff. *Borders* Genine Smith.

Glossary 17: *t.r.* Dan McGowan. *m.l.* Richard Cowdrey. *b.r.* Dale Gustafson. 18: Mike Quon. 19: Dale Gustafson. 20: Dan McGowan. 21,22: Dale Gustafson. 23: Robert Roper. 24: A.J. Miller. 26,27: Patrick Gnan. 28: Hans & Cassady Inc. 29: Dan McGowan. 30: Hans & Cassady Inc. 32: David Barber. 33: Patrick Gnan.

PHOTOGRAPHS

All photographs by Houghton Mifflin Company (HMCo.) unless otherwise noted.

Cover *t.* Superstock; *m.l.* Bill Brooks/Masterfile Corporation; *m.r.* Tim Flach/Tony Stone Images; *b.l.* Barbara Leslie/FPG International; *b.r.* Greg Ryan & Sally Beyer/Tony Stone Images.

Table of Contents iv: *l.* Harold Sund/The Image Bank; *r.* Cromosohm/Sohm/The Stock Market. viii: Stan Osolinski/The Stock Market. xiii: *t.r.* Brian Parker/Tom Stack & Associates; *b.l.* Tony Freeman/PhotoEdit; *b.m.* Buff Corsi/Tom Stack & Associates; *b.r.* Gary Withey/Bruce Coleman Incorporated. xiv: © 2000 Juha Jormanainen/Woodfin Camp & Associates. xv: *l.* NOAA; *r.* NOAA/NESDIS/NCDC/SDSD.

Think Like a Scientist 2: *t. bkgd.* PhotoDisc, Inc. 3: *t.* PhotoDisc, Inc. 4–5: *bkgd.* Chip Henderson Photography.

Unit D 1: Kennan Ward/The Stock Market. 2–3: Kennan Ward/The Stock Market. 4–5: *bkgd.* © Thomas Porett/Photo Researchers, Inc.; *inset* Grace Moore for HMCo. 6–7: Ken Karp for HMCo. 7: Ken Karp for HMCo. 10: Ken Karp for HMCo. 14: © 2000 Thomas Raupach/Woodfin Camp & Associates. 16: Ken Karp for HMCo. 17: Ken Karp for HMCo. 18: Ken Karp for HMCo. 23: *l.* E.R. Degginger/Color-Pic, Inc.; *r.* Science Exploratorium. 24: S. Nielsen/Imagery. 26–27: *bkgd.* Bob McKeever/Tom Stack & Associates; *inset* Billy Hustace. 27: © Dave Archer/Space Art, San Rafael, California. 28: Grant Huntington for HMCo. 29: Grant Huntington for HMCo. 31: Grant Huntington for HMCo. 32: *t.l.* Grant Huntington for HMCo.; *t.r.* Grant Huntington for HMCo.; *b.* Grant Huntington for HMCo. 34: Ulf E. Wallin/The Image Bank. 36: Grant Huntington for HMCo. 37: *l.* Grant Huntington for HMCo.; *r.* Grant Huntington for HMCo. 39: Grant Huntington for HMCo. 40: *t.l.* David Young-Wolff/PhotoEdit; *t.m.* Tony Freeman/PhotoEdit; *b.l.* David Young-Wolff/PhotoEdit; *b.m.* David Young-Wolff/PhotoEdit; *b.r.* David Young-Wolff/PhotoEdit. 42: Grant Huntington for HMCo. 45: Grant Huntington for HMCo. 47: Grant Huntington for HMCo. 49: *t.* North Wind Picture Archives; *b.l.* The Granger Collection, New York; *b.r.* Stock Montage, Inc. 54: Adelina Mejia-Zelaya. 57: *t.* Ken Karp for HMCo.; *b.* Ken Karp for HMCo. 58–59: *t.* Tony Freeman/PhotoEdit; *b.* John Neubauer/PhotoEdit. 59: Peter Lambert/Tony Stone Images. 64: *t.* © 2000 Dewitt Jones/Woodfin Camp & Associates; *b.* © Lawrence Livermore/Science Photo Library/Photo Researchers, Inc. 65: *t.* Dan McCoy/Rainbow; *b.l.* Michael Newman/PhotoEdit; *b.r.* Ulrike Welsch/PhotoEdit. 66: *l.* Ken Karp for HMCo.; *r.* Ken Karp for HMCo. 67: Ken Karp for HMCo. 70–71: Deborah Davis/PhotoEdit. 71: Russ Kinne/Comstock. 73: *t.* © Mark Boulton/Photo Researchers, Inc.; *b.* Sipa Press. 76: *t.* Tony Freeman/PhotoEdit; *b.l.* Tony Freeman/PhotoEdit; *b.r.* Tony Freeman/PhotoEdit. 77: Russ Kinne/Comstock.

Glossary 19: Buff Corsi/Tom Stack & Associates. 25: E.R. Degginger/Color-Pic, Inc. 31: Gary Withey/Bruce Coleman Incorporated.

Teaching Guide

ILLUSTRATORS

Cover Genine Smith.

Contributing Artists Garry Colby, Jim Effier, Genine Smith, Nancy Tobin, David Winter.

PHOTOGRAPHS

All photographs by Houghton Mifflin Company (HMCo.) unless otherwise noted.

T2–T3: Dan Levinski/Masterfile Corporation. T3: J. Carmichael/The Image Bank. 1: Kennan Ward/The Stock Market. 1f: *t.l.* Courtesy, Beverly Hannahan; *t.r.* Courtesy, Cheryl Stephens; *b.* Courtesy, Richard Bollinger. 1q: © Disney. 1r: *bkgd.* PhotoDisc, Inc. 1s: Grant Huntington for HMCo.

SCIENCE and MATH TOOLBOX

H1

Using a
Hand Lens

A hand lens is a tool that magnifies objects, or makes objects appear larger. This makes it possible for you to see details of an object that would be hard to see without the hand lens.

▲ Place the lens above the object.

▲ Move the lens slowly toward you.

Look at a Coin or a Stamp

1. Place an object such as a coin or a stamp on a table or other flat surface.

2. Hold the hand lens just above the object. As you look through the lens, slowly move the lens away from the object. Notice that the object appears to get larger.

3. Keep moving the lens until the object begins to look a little blurry. Then move the hand lens a little closer to the object until the object is once again in sharp focus.

If the object starts to look blurry, move the lens toward the object. ▶

H2

Making a
Bar Graph

A bar graph helps you organize and compare data.

Make a Bar Graph of Animal Heights

Animals come in all different shapes and sizes. You can use the information in the table to make a bar graph of animal heights.

Heights of Animals	
Animal	Height (cm)
Bear	240
Elephant	315
Cow	150
Giraffe	570
Camel	210
Horse	165

1. Draw the side and the bottom of the graph. Label the side of the graph as shown. The numbers will show the height of the animals in centimeters.

3. Choose a title for your graph. Your title should describe the subject of the graph.

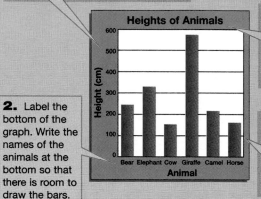

2. Label the bottom of the graph. Write the names of the animals at the bottom so that there is room to draw the bars.

4. Draw bars to show the height of each animal. Some heights are between two numbers.

H3

Using a
Hand Lens

Helpful Hints Hand lenses are listed as 3X, 6X, 8X, etc. This means that the usual maximum magnification is, in the case of the 3X, 3 times the size of the object. In order to attain the greatest magnification, the lens must be held away from the eye.

Try It Out
- Have your students inspect a sheet of graph paper with a hand lens. When the squares are as large as possible, how many squares do they see? How many squares can they see when the lens is held near the eye?
- Placing one lens directly on top of an identical lens doubles the magnification. Have your students try it. Can they find Lincoln's statue in the Lincoln Memorial on a penny? Can they find the designer's initials under Lincoln's shoulder on the face of the penny?

Making a
Bar Graph

Helpful Hints A good bar graph always has a title and horizontal and vertical axes that are labeled to show what they represent. The label at the base of each bar may be a word or a symbol. If it is a symbol, the graph should include a Key or Legend that tells what each symbol means. If the axis parallel to the bars shows relative numbers, it should be scaled from zero at its base. If it shows measurements, the unit of measure (e.g., cm) should appear in parentheses near the axis label. Bars may be oriented in either a horizontal or vertical direction. The choice of direction may make the graph more meaningful.

Try It Out
- Bar graphs are best used for representing categories that do not have continuous values. Have students prepare bar graphs representing the number of students in each grade in the school.

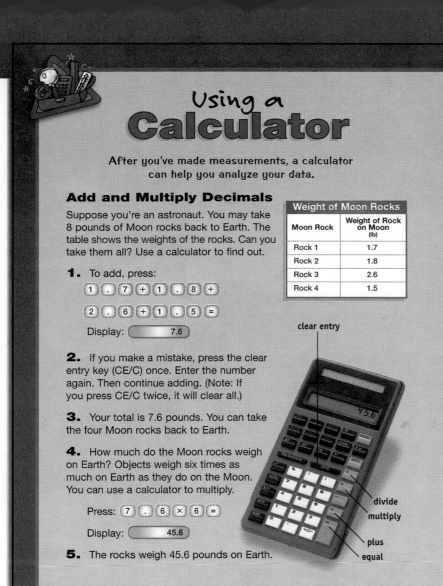

Using a Calculator

After you've made measurements, a calculator can help you analyze your data.

Add and Multiply Decimals

Suppose you're an astronaut. You may take 8 pounds of Moon rocks back to Earth. The table shows the weights of the rocks. Can you take them all? Use a calculator to find out.

Weight of Moon Rocks	
Moon Rock	Weight of Rock on Moon (lb)
Rock 1	1.7
Rock 2	1.8
Rock 3	2.6
Rock 4	1.5

1. To add, press:

1 . 7 + 1 . 8 +

2 . 6 + 1 . 5 =

Display: 7.6

2. If you make a mistake, press the clear entry key (CE/C) once. Enter the number again. Then continue adding. (Note: If you press CE/C twice, it will clear all.)

3. Your total is 7.6 pounds. You can take the four Moon rocks back to Earth.

4. How much do the Moon rocks weigh on Earth? Objects weigh six times as much on Earth as they do on the Moon. You can use a calculator to multiply.

Press: 7 . 6 × 6 =

Display: 45.6

5. The rocks weigh 45.6 pounds on Earth.

clear entry

divide
multiply
plus
equal

H4

Finding an Average

An average is a way to describe a group of numbers. For example, after you have made a series of measurements, you can find the average. This can help you analyze your data.

Add and Divide to Find the Average

The table shows the amount of rain that fell each month for the first six months of the year. What was the average rainfall per month?

Rainfall	
Month	Rain (mm)
Jan.	102
Feb.	75
Mar.	46
Apr.	126
May	51
June	32

1. Add the numbers in the list.

```
 102 ⎫
  75 ⎪
  46 ⎬ 6 addends
 126 ⎪
  51 ⎪
+ 32 ⎭
 432
```

2. Divide the sum (432) by the number of addends (6).

```
      72
  6 ) 432
    − 42
      12
    − 12
       0
```

3. The average rainfall per month for the first six months was 72 mm of rain.

H5

Using a Calculator

Helpful Hints Calculators are great tools but they have one fault. They always give an answer. However, if one pushes the wrong button… Try to get your students in the habit of always checking to see that the result shown on the calculator display is reasonable.

Try It Out

• Divide the class into groups of about six students. Have each group member trace an outline of his or her shoe on a sheet of paper and cut it out. Within groups measure the length of each shoe in centimeters. If placed end-to-end, how far will the shoe outlines reach? Use the calculator to find the total length.

• Record each group's total length on the chalkboard. Have the groups use calculators to find the total length of all the feet.

Finding an Average

Helpful Hints Scientists often find the average (mean) value for their data. In any experiment where multiple repetitions would be expected to give the same result, the average is used as the best estimate of that result. Of course, there are always errors due to human observation and experimental conditions. The smaller the errors the more uniform are the results.

Students should learn that experiments should be repeated to provide reliable answers. The repetition ideally is within the same working group. However, this is not always practical in the classroom. The results from different groups can be gathered and averaged.

Try It Out

• Provide students with data on the number of minutes spent in science class each day for a week. Have students find the average amount of time spent in science class daily.

Using a
Tape Measure or Ruler

Tape measures and rulers are tools for measuring the length of objects and distances. Scientists most often use units such as meters, centimeters, and millimeters when making length measurements.

Use a Tape Measure

1. Measure the distance around a jar. Wrap the tape around the jar.

2. Find the line where the tape begins to wrap over itself.

3. Record the distance around the jar to the nearest centimeter.

Use a Metric Ruler

1. Measure the length of your shoe. Place the ruler or the meterstick on the floor. Line up the end of the ruler with the heel of your shoe.

2. Notice where the other end of your shoe lines up with the ruler.

3. Look at the scale on the ruler. Record the length of your shoe to the nearest centimeter and to the nearest millimeter.

Measuring
Volume

A graduated cylinder, a measuring cup, and a beaker are used to measure volume. Volume is the amount of space something takes up. Most of the containers that scientists use to measure volume have a scale marked in milliliters (mL).

Measure the Volume of a Liquid

1. Measure the volume of juice. Pour some juice into a measuring container.

2. Move your head so that your eyes are level with the top of the juice. Read the scale line that is closest to the surface of the juice. If the surface of the juice is curved up on the sides, look at the lowest point of the curve.

3. Read the measurement on the scale. You can estimate the value between two lines on the scale.

▲ The bottom of the curve is at 35 mL.

This beaker has marks for each 25 mL. ▶

This graduated cylinder has marks for every 1 mL. ▶

▲ This measuring cup has marks for each 25 mL.

Using a
Tape Measure or Ruler

Helpful Hints Tape measures often have ends that are ragged or deformed. Such tape measures may still be used by measuring from the one centimeter mark, and then subtracting one from the result. Occasionally, rulers suffer from the same problem.

Try It Out

• Measuring round or irregularly shaped objects is often a problem. Have your students measure the diameter of a ball. Challenge them to devise an accurate method. The easiest way to do it is to place the ball between two vertical planes, such as two books. Then measure the distance between the planes.

Measuring
Volume

Helpful Hints Containers that are graduated to measure volume always have a range of error. (In fact, the same can be said for all measuring instruments.) Usually, the smaller the diameter of the container, the more accurate it is. Graduated cylinders are much more accurate than measuring cups designed for the kitchen. Beakers that have graduations on the sides are only approximate.

Try It Out

• Have students use a measuring cup to find the volume of a liquid. Then have them use a graduated cylinder to determine the volume again. Have students discuss the reason for any difference.

Using a
Thermometer

A thermometer is used to measure temperature. When the liquid in the tube of a thermometer gets warmer, it expands and moves farther up the tube. Different scales can be used to measure temperature, but scientists usually use the Celsius scale.

Measure the Temperature of a Cold Liquid

1. Take a chilled liquid out of the refrigerator. Half fill a cup with the liquid.

2. Hold the thermometer so that the bulb is in the center of the liquid. Be sure that there are no bright lights or direct sunlight shining on the bulb.

3. Wait a few minutes until you see the liquid in the tube of the thermometer stop moving. Read the scale line that is closest to the top of the liquid in the tube. The thermometer shown reads 21°C (about 70°F).

Using a
Balance

A balance is used to measure mass. Mass is the amount of matter in an object. To find the mass of an object, place it in the left pan of the balance. Place standard masses in the right pan.

Measure the Mass of a Ball

1. Check that the empty pans are balanced, or level with each other. When balanced, the pointer on the base should be at the middle mark. If it needs to be adjusted, move the slider on the back of the balance a little to the left or right.

2. Place a ball on the left pan. Then add standard masses, one at a time, to the right pan. When the pointer is at the middle mark again, each pan holds the same amount of matter and has the same mass.

3. Add the numbers marked on the masses in the pan. The total is the mass of the ball in grams.

Using a
Thermometer

Helpful Hints When using a thermometer to measure the temperature of a liquid, the thermometer should be read with the bulb still immersed in the liquid. Otherwise, the liquid in the bulb will begin to expand or contract immediately after it is removed.

When measuring air temperatures, students have a tendency to hold the bottom of the thermometer. In order not to affect the reading, they should keep their fingers well away from the bulb.

Try It Out

• Divide your class into groups. Give each group equal volumes of warm and cold water in plastic foam cups. Have each group measure the temperature of the water in both cups. Then have them predict the temperature of the water when combined. Have students try it. The resulting temperature will be halfway between the two.

Using a
Balance

Helpful Hints Teach students to place the object they are measuring on the left-hand pan. Then they will not have a problem when they later encounter balances that have a mass that slides from left to right.

After the balance has been zero adjusted, it should not be moved. Another location might cause the pointer to move off zero.

Try It Out

• Do some paper towels absorb more water than others? Since water has mass, and so do paper towels, the balance is a good instrument to use in determining the answer. Have your students, in teams, design an experiment to solve the problem.

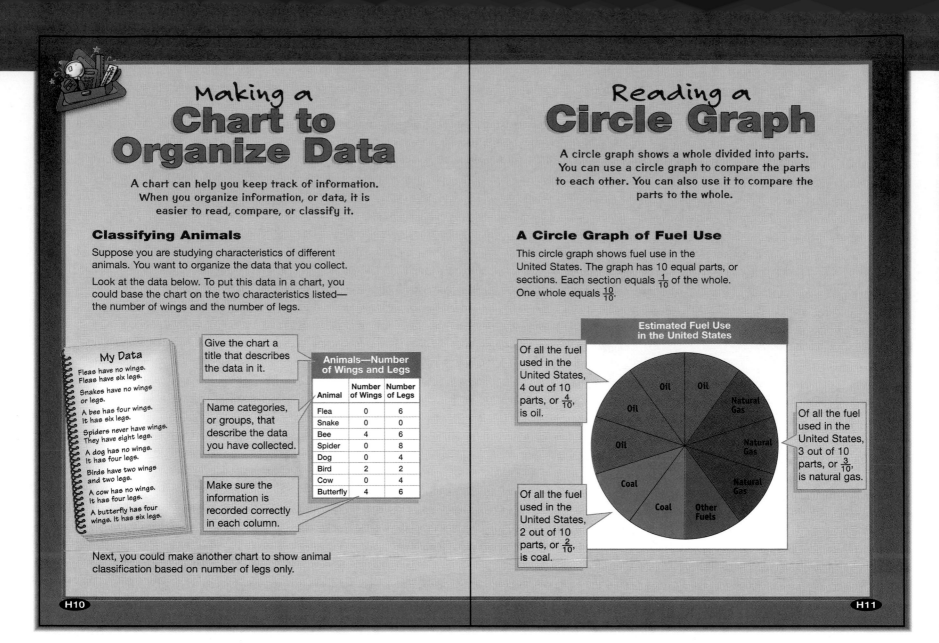

Making a
Chart to Organize Data

Helpful Hints When children do science experiments, they should always make data charts to record their observations. The chart might be kept by individual students, a working group, or you. In any case, the chart, or table, should have a title, columns for data, and column headers that tell what data is in each column. If a column in a chart contains measurements, the unit of measure should appear in the column header. This eliminates the need to write the unit after each measurement in the column.

Try It Out

• If you have a computer with a spreadsheet program, have students set up their data charts on the spreadsheet. If you aggregate data from teams following a science activity, you might consider having one or two students input the data as it is reported. Then duplicate the class data for each student.

Reading a
Circle Graph

Helpful Hints Circle graphs make it easy to compare subsets of data. Because data has to be converted to degrees or fractions, circle graphs can be more difficult to prepare than bar graphs. At this age, the emphasis should be on interpreting circle graphs.

Try It Out

• Collect circle graphs from news magazines and newspapers. Distribute them and ask students to write descriptions of what they show. Discuss the advantages of circle graphs over a written paragraph.

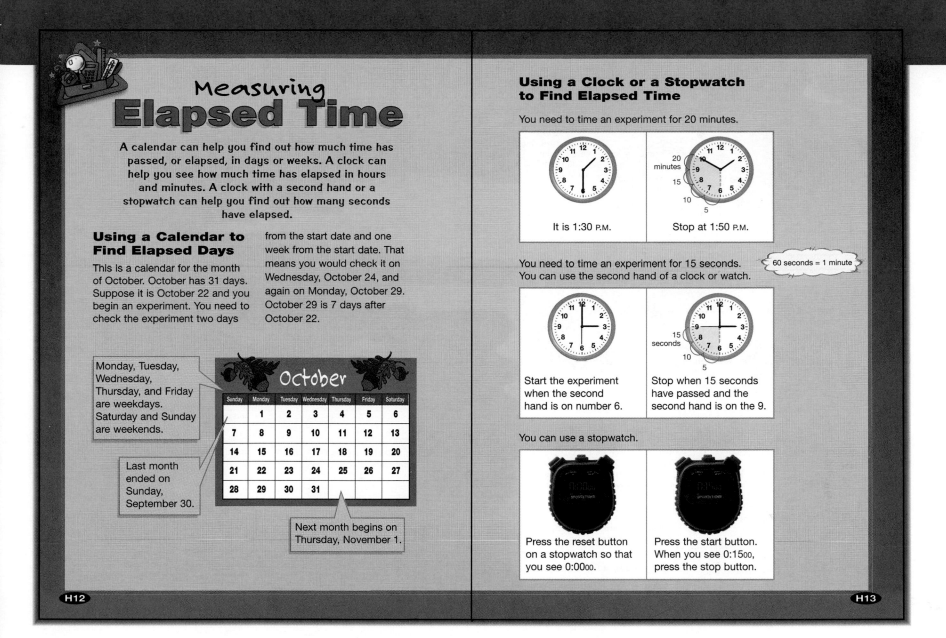

Measuring Elapsed Time

A calendar can help you find out how much time has passed, or elapsed, in days or weeks. A clock can help you see how much time has elapsed in hours and minutes. A clock with a second hand or a stopwatch can help you find out how many seconds have elapsed.

Using a Calendar to Find Elapsed Days

This is a calendar for the month of October. October has 31 days. Suppose it is October 22 and you begin an experiment. You need to check the experiment two days from the start date and one week from the start date. That means you would check it on Wednesday, October 24, and again on Monday, October 29. October 29 is 7 days after October 22.

Monday, Tuesday, Wednesday, Thursday, and Friday are weekdays. Saturday and Sunday are weekends.

Last month ended on Sunday, September 30.

October

Sunday	Monday	Tuesday	Wednesday	Thursday	Friday	Saturday
	1	2	3	4	5	6
7	8	9	10	11	12	13
14	15	16	17	18	19	20
21	22	23	24	25	26	27
28	29	30	31			

Next month begins on Thursday, November 1.

Using a Clock or a Stopwatch to Find Elapsed Time

You need to time an experiment for 20 minutes.

It is 1:30 P.M.

Stop at 1:50 P.M.

You need to time an experiment for 15 seconds. You can use the second hand of a clock or watch.

60 seconds = 1 minute

Start the experiment when the second hand is on number 6.

Stop when 15 seconds have passed and the second hand is on the 9.

You can use a stopwatch.

Press the reset button on a stopwatch so that you see 0:00oo.

Press the start button. When you see 0:15oo, press the stop button.

H12

H13

Measuring Elapsed Time

Helpful Hints Estimating time intervals is difficult for many people. In many science experiments, an accurate measurement of how long an event took to occur is an important piece of data. Emphasize with students that finding elapsed time is part of data collection in science.

Try It Out

- Use your classroom clock to determine the time elapsed since the school day started, until recess, and so on. Ask students which is easier for figuring elapsed time, a clock with a circular dial or a digital clock?

- How much time must elapse before your next school holiday? Students could number, in reverse order, days on a calendar from that date.

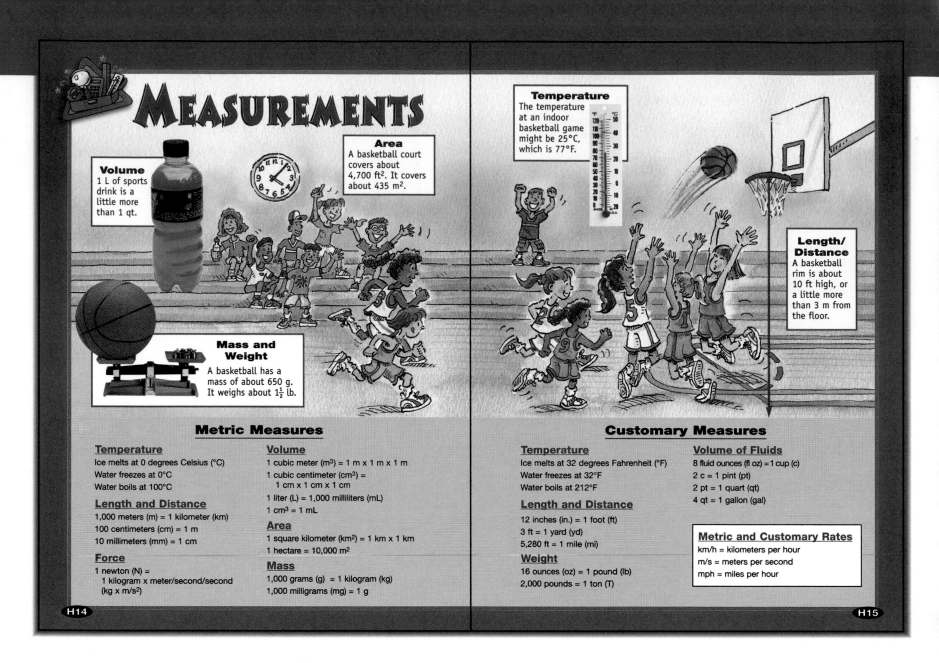

MEASUREMENTS

It is usually not a good idea to ask students to convert values from one measuring system to another. When metric measurements are required, use metric tools; similarly, when customary measurements are needed, use the appropriate instruments. However, some relational benchmarks are useful. For example:

1 cm	is a generous	1/2 inch
1 meter	is a generous	1 yard
1 liter	is a generous	1 quart
1 kilogram	is a generous	2 pounds
1 kilometer	is a generous	1/2 mile

Room temperature is about 20˚C.
Hot tap water is usually about 40˚C.

If conversions are necessary, use a simple graph to do it. For a temperature conversion, make a graph with Celsius temperatures on one axis and Fahrenheit on the other. Locate and mark two points using these temperatures as coordinates: (0˚C, 32˚F) and (100˚C, 212˚F).

Then draw a straight line through both points. To convert from one temperature scale to another, read across (or up) from one axis to the line and then down (or across) to the other axis. The same technique may be used with length, mass, or volume. All that is needed are two points to establish the line.

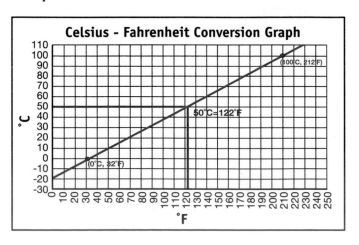

GLOSSARY

Pronunciation Key

Symbol	Key Words	Symbol	Key Words
a	cat	g	get
ā	ape	h	help
ä	cot, car	j	jump
		k	kiss, call
e	ten, berry	l	leg
ē	me	m	meat
		n	nose
i	fit, here	p	put
ī	ice, fire	r	red
		s	see
ō	go	t	top
ô	fall, for	v	vat
oi	oil	w	wish
o͞o	look, pull	y	yard
o͞o	tool, rule	z	zebra
ou	out, crowd		
		ch	chin, arch
u	up	ŋ	ring, drink
u	fur, shirt	sh	she, push
		th	thin, truth
ə	a in ago	*th*	then, father
	e in agent	zh	measure
	i in pencil		
	o in atom	A heavy stress mark (′) is	
	u in circus	placed after a syllable that gets	
		a heavy, or primary, stress, as	
b	bed	in **picture** (pik′chər).	
d	dog		
f	fall		

H16

---

adaptation (ad əp tā′shən) A part or behavior that makes a living thing better able to survive in its environment. (C54) The spider's behavior of spinning a web to catch an insect, such as a bee, is an *adaptation* that helps the spider get food

air (er) The invisible, odorless, and tasteless mixture of gases that surrounds Earth. (E10) *Air* consists mainly of the gases nitrogen and oxygen.

air mass (er mas) A large body of air that has about the same temperature, air pressure, and moisture throughout. (E62) When warm and cold *air masses* meet, the weather changes.

air pressure (er presh′ər) The push of the air in all directions against its surroundings. (E31) You can see the effect of *air pressure* when you blow up a balloon.

amphibian (am fib′ē ən) A vertebrate that usually lives in water in the early part of its life; it breathes with gills and then later develops lungs. (C19) Frogs, toads, and salamanders are *amphibians*.

anemometer (an ə mäm′ət ər) A device used to measure the speed of the wind. (E39) The *anemometer* showed that the wind was blowing at 33 km/h.

atmosphere (at′məs fir) The blanket of air that surrounds Earth, reaching to about 700 km above the surface. (E12) Earth's *atmosphere* makes it possible for life to exist on the planet.

H17

---

atom (at′əm) The smallest part of an element that still has the properties of that element. (B30) Water forms when *atoms* of the elements hydrogen and oxygen combine in a certain way.

axis (ak′sis) An imaginary straight line from the North Pole, through Earth's center, to the South Pole. (E78) Earth makes one complete turn on its *axis* in about 24 hours.

axis

barometer (bə räm′ət ər) A device used to measure air pressure. (E30) Scientists use a *barometer* to gather information about the weather.

bay (bā) Part of a sea or lake extending into the land. (A14) The ship sailed through the *bay* into the Atlantic Ocean.

behavior (bē hāv′yər) The way in which a living thing acts or responds to its environment. (C55) Purring, washing themselves, and hunting mice are three common *behaviors* of cats.

bird (bʉrd) A vertebrate that has wings, is covered with feathers, and hatches from a hard-shell egg. (C21) A *bird* is the only organism in the animal kingdom that has feathers covering its body.

boiling (boil′iŋ) The rapid change of state from a liquid to a gas. (B40) When water is *boiling*, bubbles of water vapor form.

carbon dioxide (kär′bən dī äks′īd) A colorless, odorless gas. (E10) Plants use *carbon dioxide* from the air in the process of making food.

chemical change (kem′i kəl chānj) A change in matter that results in one or more different kinds of matter forming. (B56) A *chemical change* occurs when matter, such as paper, burns and forms gases and ash.

chemical formula (kem′i kəl fôr′myo͞o lə) A group of symbols that shows the kinds and number of atoms in a single unit of a compound. (B35) The *chemical formula* for carbon dioxide is CO_2.

chemical property (kem′i kəl präp′ər tē) A characteristic of a substance that can only be seen when the substance changes and a new substance is formed; describes how matter reacts with other matter. (B13, B56) A *chemical property* of iron is that iron can combine with oxygen to form rust.

chemical reaction (kem′i kəl rē ak′shən) The process in which one or more substances are changed into one or more different substances. (B57) A *chemical reaction* takes place when burning wood changes to ash.

chemical symbol (kem′i kəl sim′bəl) One or two letters that stand for the name of an element. (B30) The *chemical symbol* for gold is Au.

circuit breaker (sʉr′kit brāk′ər) A switch that opens or closes a circuit by turning off or on. (D52) When a circuit overheats, the *circuit breaker* switches off and the lights go out.

cirrus cloud (sir′əs kloud) A thin, feathery cloud made up of ice crystals high in the sky. (E57) *Cirrus clouds* often look like wisps of hair.

climate (klī′mət) The average weather conditions of an area over a long period of time. (E84) Some regions have a hot, rainy *climate*.

cloud (kloud) A mass of tiny droplets of water that condensed from the air. (E46) A dark *cloud* blocked the sunlight.

cold front (kōld frunt) The leading edge of a cold air mass that forms as the cold air mass moves into a warm air mass. (E62) Thunderstorms often occur along a *cold front*.

compass (kum′pəs) A device containing a magnetized needle that moves freely and is used to show direction. (D23) The north pole of the needle in a *compass* points toward Earth's magnetic north pole.

H19

compound (käm'pound)
Matter made up of two or more
elements chemically combined. (B33)
Salt is a *compound* made up of
sodium and chlorine.

condensation (kän dən sā'shən)
The change of state from a gas to a
liquid. (B42) Drops of water form on
the outside of a very cold glass
because of the *condensation* of
water vapor in the air.

condense (kən dens') To change
from a gas to a liquid. (E46) Water
vapor from the air *condenses* on a
cold window.

conductor (kən duk'tər) A material through which electricity
moves easily. (D42) Copper wire is
a good *conductor* of electricity.

conifers (kän'ə fərz) Cone-
bearing plants. (C37) Pines and fir
trees are examples of *conifers*.

conservation (kän sər vā'shən)
The preserving and wise use of
natural resources. (A31) The *conservation* of forests is important to
both humans and wildlife.

controlled experiment (kən-
trōld' ek sper'ə mənt) A test of a
hypothesis in which the setups are
identical in all ways except one. (S7)
In the *controlled experiment*, one
beaker of water contained salt.

cumulus cloud (kyōō'myōō ləs
kloud) A large puffy cloud. (E55)
White *cumulus clouds* can often
be seen in an otherwise clear
summer sky.

delta (del'tə) A flat, usually tri-
angular plain formed by deposits of
sediment where a river empties into
the ocean. (A12) The largest *delta*
in the United States is at the mouth
of the Mississippi River.

density (den'sə tē) The property
that describes how much matter is in
a given space, or volume. (B9, B11)
The *density* of air varies with its
temperature.

dicot (dī'kät) A flowering plant
that produces seeds that have two
sections. (C38) A trait of a *dicot* is
that the veins of its leaves form a
branching pattern.

electric cell (ē lek'trik sel) A
device that changes chemical energy to electrical energy. (D60)
A battery in a flashlight consists of
one or more *electric cells*.

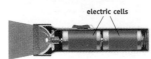
electric cells

electric charge (ē lek'trik chärj)
The electrical property of particles
of matter; an electric charge can be
positive or negative. (D30) Rubbing
a balloon with a wool cloth causes
negative *electric charges* to move
from the wool to the balloon.

electric circuit (ē lek'trik sur'kit)
A path along which an electric current can move. (D41) We made an
electric circuit, using a battery,
wires, and a light bulb.

electric current (ē lek'trik
kur'ənt) A continuous flow of
electric charges. (D41) *Electric
current* in wires allows you to run
electric appliances, such as an iron
or refrigerator, in your home.

electric discharge (ē lek'trik
dis'chärj) The loss or release of an
electric charge. (D33) A bolt of
lightning is an *electric discharge*.

electromagnet (ē lek'trō mag nit)
A magnet made when an electric
current passes through a wire coiled
around an iron core. (D70) A large
electromagnet can be strong
enough to lift heavy metal objects
such as cars.

element (el'ə mənt) Matter made
up of only one kind of atom. (B30)
Iron, oxygen, and aluminum are
three examples of *elements*.

energy (en'ər jē) The ability to
cause change. (B39) Most automo-
biles use *energy* from gasoline to
move.

environment (en vī'rən mənt)
Everything that surrounds and
affects a living thing. (C44) Desert
animals and forest animals live in
very different *environments*.

H20

H21

equator (ē kwāt'ər) An imaginary
line circling the middle of Earth,
halfway between the North Pole and
the South Pole. (E78) The *equator*
divides Earth into the Northern
Hemisphere and the Southern
Hemisphere.

erosion (ē rō'zhən) The gradual
wearing away and removing of rock
material by forces such as moving
water, wind, and moving ice. (A10)
Ocean waves cause *erosion* of the
seashore.

evaporate (ē vap'ə rāt) To
change from a liquid to a gas. (E46)
Some of the water boiling in the pot
evaporated.

evaporation (ē vap ə rā'shən)
The change of state from a liquid to
a gas. (B40) Under the hot sun,
water in a puddle changes to water
vapor through the process of
evaporation.

exoskeleton (eks ō skel'ə tən)
A hard outer structure, such as a
shell, that protects or supports an
animal's body. (C15) A lobster has
a thick *exoskeleton*.

extinct (ek stiŋkt') No longer
living as a species. (C58) Traces of
some *extinct* species can be found
in fossils.

ferns (furnz) Spore-forming plants
that have roots, stems, and leaves.
(C36) *Ferns* that grow in tropical
places have very tall fronds.

filament (fil'ə mənt) A long, thin
coil of wire that glows when electricity passes through it. (D48) The
filament in an incandescent light
bulb gives off light.

filament

fish (fish) A vertebrate that lives in
water and has gills used for breathing
and fins used for swimming. (C18)
Sharks and tuna are kinds of *fish*.

flash flood (flash flud) A sudden,
violent flood. (E67) Heavy rains
caused *flash floods* as the stream
overflowed.

fog (fôg) A cloud that touches
Earth's surface. (E46) Traffic acci-
dents often increase where *fog* is
heavy.

fossil fuel (fäs'əl fyōō'əl) A fuel
that formed from the remains of
once-living things and that is nonrenewable. (A47) Oil is a *fossil fuel*.

freezing (frēz'iŋ) The change of
state from a liquid to a solid. (B42)
Water turns to ice by *freezing*.

front (frunt) The place where two
air masses meet. (E62) Forecasters
watch the movement of *fronts* to
help predict the weather.

cold front

fuse (fyōōz) A device in a circuit
that contains a metal strip, which
melts when the circuit is overheated,
thus breaking the circuit. (D52) The
fuse blew because too many appliances were connected to the same
electric circuit.

gas (gas) The state of matter that
has no definite shape or volume.
(B29) Helium is a very light *gas* that
is used to fill some balloons.

generator (jen'ər āt ər) A device
that changes energy of motion into
electrical energy. (D58) The huge
generator uses water power to produce electricity.

gill (gil) A feathery structure on
each side of a fish's head that lets
the fish breathe underwater. (C18) A
fish takes in oxygen through its *gills*.

glacier (glā'shər) A huge mass of
slow-moving ice that forms over
land; glaciers form in areas where
the amount of snow that falls is
more than the amount of snow that
melts. (A22) As it moves, a *glacier*
changes the surface beneath it.

greenhouse effect (grēn'hous
e fekt') The process by which heat
from the Sun builds up near Earth's
surface and is trapped by the atmosphere. (E15) Some scientists fear
that air pollution may increase the
greenhouse effect and raise temperatures on Earth.

hazardous waste (haz'ər dəs
wāst) A waste material that dirties
the environment and that can kill living things or cause disease. (A65)
Some chemicals used to kill insects
become *hazardous wastes*.

H22

H23

headland (hed′lənd) A piece of land that extends out into the water and usually slows down the flow of water that passes it. (A14) The lighthouse stood on a *headland* overlooking the bay.

high-pressure area (hī presh′ər er′ē ə) An area of higher air pressure than that of the surrounding air. (E33) Winds move from *high-pressure areas* to low-pressure areas.

horsetails (hôrs tālz) Plants that reproduce by spores and have underground stems. (C36) *Horsetails* are also known as scouring rushes because of the tough tip at the end of their bamboo-like stem.

humidity (hyōō mid′ə tē) The amount of water vapor in the air. (E47) Tropical climates have warm temperatures and high *humidity*.

hurricane (hʉr′i kān) A large, violent storm accompanied by strong winds and, usually, heavy rain. (E70) The winds of the *hurricane* blew at over 125 km/h.

hypothesis (hī päth′ə sis) An idea about or explanation of how or why something happens. (S6) The *hypothesis* about the expanding universe has been supported by evidence gathered by astronomers.

H24

ice age (īs āj) A period of time when glaciers covered much of Earth's land. (E89) During the last *ice age,* glaciers covered parts of North America.

incineration (in sin ər ā′shən) Burning to ashes. (A60) You can get rid of trash by *incineration*.

instinctive behavior (in stiŋk′tiv bē hāv′yər) A behavior that a living thing does naturally without having to learn it. (C56) For a mother bird, feeding her young is an *instinctive behavior*.

insulator (in′sə lāt ər) A material through which electricity does not move easily. (D42) Rubber can prevent an electric shock because rubber is a good *insulator*.

invertebrate (in vʉr′tə brit) An animal that does not have a backbone. (C15) *Invertebrates* include jellyfish, sponges, insects, and worms.

---

landfill (land′fil) An area where trash is buried and covered over with dirt. (A59) In some places, towns decide to build recreation areas, such as parks, on the sites of old *landfills*.

learned behavior (lʉrnd bē hāv′yər) A behavior that an organism is taught or learns from experience. (C56) Sitting on command, catching a ball, and jumping through a hoop are examples of *learned behavior* for a dog.

lines of force (līnz uv fôrs) The lines that form a pattern showing the size and shape of a magnetic force field. (D19) Iron filings sprinkled over a magnet form *lines of force* that show the strength and the direction of the magnet's force.

liquid (lik′wid) The state of matter that has a definite volume but no definite shape. (B29) A *liquid*, such as water or milk, takes the shape of its container.

litter (lit′ər) The trash that is discarded on the ground or in water rather than being disposed of properly. (A66) The children cleaned up the park by removing all the *litter* they could find.

liverworts (liv′ər wʉrts) Nonseed plants that lack true roots, stems, and leaves. (C36) The logs by the stream were covered with mosslike *liverworts*.

lodestone (lōd′stōn) A naturally magnetic mineral found at or near Earth's surface. (D22) A piece of *lodestone* will attract iron.

low-pressure area (lō presh′ər er′ē ə) An area of lower air pressure than that of the surrounding air. (E33) Storms are more likely to occur in *low-pressure areas*.

---

magnet (mag′nit) An object that has the property of attracting certain materials, mainly iron and steel. (D11) The girl used a horseshoe *magnet* to pick up paper clips.

magnetic field (mag net′ik fēld) The space around a magnet within which the force of the magnet can act. (D20) The magnet attracted all the pins within its *magnetic field*.

H25

---

magnetism (mag′nə tiz əm) A magnet's property of attracting certain materials, mainly iron and steel. (D11) *Magnetism* keeps kitchen magnets attached to a refrigerator door.

mammal (mam′əl) A vertebrate, such as a cat, that has hair or fur and feeds its young with milk. (C22) Dogs, cats, rabbits, deer, bats, horses, mice, elephants, whales, and humans are all *mammals*.

mass (mas) The amount of matter that something contains. (B10) A large rock has more *mass* than a small rock that is made of the same material.

matter (mat′ər) Anything that has mass and takes up space. (B10) Rocks, water, and air are three kinds of *matter*.

melting (melt′iŋ) The change of state from a solid to a liquid. (B40) As the temperature of the air rises, snow and ice change to liquid water by the process of *melting*.

H26

metric system (me′trik sis′təm) A system of measurement in which the number of smaller parts in each unit is based on the number 10 and multiples of 10. (B20) Centimeters, meters, and kilometers are units of length in the *metric system*.

mineral (min′ər əl) A solid, found in nature, that has a definite chemical makeup. (A41) Salt, coal, diamond, and gold are some examples of *minerals*.

mixture (miks′chər) Matter that is made up of two or more substances that can be separated by physical means. (B50) This salad contains a *mixture* of lettuce, cucumbers, celery, and tomatoes.

molt (mōlt) To shed an outer covering such as hair, outer skin, horns, or feathers at certain times. (C30) Snakes and insects *molt*.

monocot (män′ō kät) A flowering plant that produces seeds that are in one piece. (C38) About one third of all flowering plants are *monocots*.

mosses (môs′əs) Small nonseed plants that lack true roots, stems, and leaves. (C35) The leaflike part of *mosses* grows only a few centimeters above ground.

---

natural resource (nach′ər əl rē′sôrs) Any useful material from Earth, such as water, oil, and minerals. (A31) One reason that trees are an important *natural resource* is that their wood is used to build houses and to make paper.

nitrogen (nī′trə jən) A colorless, odorless, tasteless gas that makes up about four fifths of the air. (E10) *Nitrogen* is used by plants for growth.

nonrenewable resource (nän-ri nōō′ə bəl rē′sôrs) A natural resource that can't be replaced once it's removed. (A42) Minerals are classified as a *nonrenewable resource* because there's a limited amount of them.

nonseed plants (nän sēd plants) Plants that do not reproduce with seeds. (C35) Ferns are *nonseed plants*.

Northern Hemisphere (nôr′thərn hem′i sfir) The half of Earth north of the equator. (E79) Canada is in the *Northern Hemisphere*.

north pole (nôrth pōl) One of the ends of a magnet where the magnetic force is strongest; it points to the north when the magnet moves freely. (D13) *North poles* of magnets repel each other.

north pole

---

ore (ôr) A mineral or rock that contains enough of a metal to make mining that metal profitable. (A41) Gold, aluminum, copper, and tin come from *ores*.

organism (ôr′gə niz əm) A living thing that can be classified as belonging to one of several kingdoms. (C8) Animals and plants are *organisms*.

oxygen (äks′i jən) A colorless, odorless, tasteless gas that makes up about one fifth of the air. (E10) *Oxygen* is essential to life.

H27

packaging (pak'ij iŋ) The wrapping and containers in which items are transported or offered for sale. (A75) *Packaging* protects products from damage but adds to their cost.

parallel circuit (par'ə lel sur'kit) An electric circuit having more than one path along which electric current can travel. (D51) Because the circuits in a home are *parallel circuits*, you can switch off one light and others will stay on.

physical change (fiz'i kəl chānj) A change in size, shape, or state of matter in which no new matter is formed. (B48) Cutting an apple in half and freezing water into ice cubes are *physical changes*.

physical property (fiz'i kəl präp'ər tē) A characteristic of a material or object that can be seen or measured without changing the material into a new substance. (B12) One *physical property* of a ball is its round shape.

polar climate (pō'lər klī'mət) A very cold climate that does not receive much energy from the Sun. (E85) The Arctic has a *polar climate*.

pollutant (pə lōōt''nt) A substance that causes pollution. (A65) The exhaust gases from cars add *pollutants* to the air.

pollution (pə lōō'shən) The dirtying of the environment with waste materials or other unwanted substances. (A65) Water *pollution* can cause disease or even death in living things.

precipitation (prē sip ə tā'shən) Any form of water that falls from clouds to Earth's surface. (E46) Rain, snow, and hail are forms of *precipitation*.

property (präp'ər tē) A characteristic that describes matter. (B12) Hardness is a *property* of steel.

rain gauge (rān gāj) A device for measuring precipitation. (E47) The *rain gauge* at the weather station showed that 2 cm of rain had fallen in 24 hours.

recycle (rē sī'kəl) To process and reuse materials. (A72) Discarded newspapers are *recycled* to make new paper.

relative humidity (rel'ə tiv hyōō mid'ə tē) The amount of water vapor present in the air at a given temperature compared to the maximum amount that the air could hold at that temperature. (E47) A *relative humidity* of 95 percent on a warm day can make you feel sticky and uncomfortable.

renewable resource (ri nōō'ə bəl rē'sôrs) A resource that can be replaced. (A42) Water is a *renewable resource* because rain increases the supply of water.

reptile (rep'təl) A vertebrate, such as a lizard or a crocodile, that has dry scaly skin and lays eggs that have a leathery shell. (C20) *Reptiles* can be found in both deserts and rain forests.

river system (riv'ər sis'təm) A river and all the waterways, such as brooks, streams, and rivers, that drain into it. (A11) The Mississippi River and the many waterways feeding into it make up the largest *river system* in the country.

rock (räk) A solid material that is made up of one or more minerals and that may be used for its properties. (A41) Granite is a hard *rock* used in construction.

sand dune (sand dōōn) A mound, hill, or ridge of sand formed by the wind. (A21) *Sand dunes* are common in the desert.

sand dune

savanna (sə van'ə) A broad, grassy plain that has few or no trees. (C48) Nearly half of Africa is covered by *savannas*.

sediment (sed'ə mənt) Sand, soil, and rock carried by water, wind, or ice. (A12) The rushing water of the river deposited *sediment* along the riverbanks.

seed plants (sēd plants) Plants that reproduce with seeds. (C35) Corn and wheat are *seed plants*.

series circuit (sir'ēz sur'kit) An electric circuit in which the parts are connected in a single path. (D50) Electric current can follow only one path in a *series circuit*.

soil (soil) Loose material that covers much of Earth's land surface and is made up of three layers—topsoil, subsoil, and partly weathered rock. (A30) Plants, insects, and worms live in *soil*.

solar cell (sō'lər sel) A device that changes sunlight into electrical energy. (D64) *Solar cells* used in power plants can produce electricity without polluting the air.

solar energy (sō'lər en'ər jē) The clean and relatively low-cost energy from the Sun. (A50, D64) *Solar energy* is used to heat water in some homes.

solid (säl'id) Matter that has a definite volume and a definite shape. (B29) A *solid*, such as a rock, a wooden block, or an ice cube, has a definite volume and shape.

solution (sə lōō'shən) A mixture in which the particles of different substances are mixed evenly. (B51) Stirring sugar into water makes a *solution*.

Southern Hemisphere (suth'ərn hem'i sfir) The half of Earth south of the equator. (E79) The island continent Australia is in the *Southern Hemisphere*.

south pole (south pōl) One of the ends of a magnet where the magnetic force is strongest; it points to the south when the magnet moves freely. (D13) The *south pole* of one magnet attracts the north pole of another magnet.

standard unit (stan'dərd yōōn'it) A unit of measure that everyone agrees to use. (B19) Scientists use the gram as the *standard unit* of mass.

state of matter (stāt uv mat'ər) Any of the three forms that matter may ordinarily take: solid, liquid, and gas. (B29) When ice melts, it changes to a liquid *state of matter*.

static electricity (stat'ik ē lek-tris'i tē) Electric charges that have built up on the surface of an object. (D31) Walking across a carpet on a cold, dry day can produce *static electricity*.

stratus cloud (strāt'əs kloud) A low, flat cloud that often brings drizzle. (E55) Large sheets of very dark *stratus clouds* covered the sky on the rainy morning.

substance (sub'stəns) A class of matter made up of elements and compounds. (B34) Salt and sugar are *substances*.

switch (swich) A device that completes or breaks the path a current can follow in an electric circuit. (D41) In order to turn on the light, you must press the *switch* to complete the circuit.

temperate climate (tem'pər it klī'mət) A climate that generally has warm, dry summers and cold, wet winters. (E85) Most regions of the United States have a *temperate climate*.

theory (thē'ə rē) A hypothesis that is supported by a lot of evidence and is widely accepted by scientists. (S9) The big-bang *theory* offers an explanation for the origin of the universe.

thunderstorm (thun'dər stôrm) A storm that produces lightning and thunder and often heavy rain and strong winds. (E66) When the weather is hazy, hot, and humid, *thunderstorms* are likely to develop.

tornado (tôr nā'dō) A violent, funnel-shaped storm of spinning wind. (E72) The wind speed at the center of a *tornado* can be twice that of hurricane winds.

tropical climate (träp'i kəl klī'mət) A hot, rainy climate. (E85) Areas that are near the equator have a *tropical climate* because they receive the greatest amount of energy from the Sun.

troposphere (trō′pō sfir) The layer of the atmosphere closest to the surface of Earth. (E12) The *troposphere* reaches about 11 km above the surface of Earth and is the layer of the atmosphere in which weather occurs.

variable (ver′ē ə bəl) The one difference in the setups of a controlled experiment; provides a comparison for testing a hypothesis. (S7) The *variable* in an experiment with plants was the amount of water given each plant.

vertebra (vʉr′tə brə) One of the bones that together make up the backbone. (C14) Each knob in your backbone is a *vertebra*.

vertebrate (vʉr′tə brit) An animal that has a backbone. (C14) Reptiles and birds are *vertebrates*.

backbone

voltage (vōl′tij) The force of an electric current, measured in volts. (D63) Electric currents of high *voltage* travel through long-distance power lines.

volume (väl yōōm) The amount of space that matter takes up. (B10) A baseball has a greater *volume* than a golf ball does.

warm front (wôrm frunt) The leading edge of a warm air mass that forms as the warm air mass moves forward into a cold air mass. (E63) Light rain often falls along a *warm front*.

water cycle (wôt′ər si′kəl) The movement of water into the air as water vapor and back to Earth's surface as rain, snow, or hail. (E46) The *water cycle* is powered by energy from the Sun.

water vapor (wôt′ər vā′pər) Water that is in the form of a gas. (E10) *Water vapor* from the air forms drops of water on cold glass surfaces.

weather (weth′ər) The condition of the atmosphere at a certain place and time. (E13) The *weather* today in Chicago is snowy.

weather forecaster (weth′ər fôr′kast ər) A person who makes weather predictions or reports weather conditions. (E61) The *weather forecaster* predicted rain for the next three days.

weather satellite (weth′ər sat′′l īt) A human-made device in space that takes pictures of Earth and collects information about the weather. (E54) The *weather satellite* sent back pictures of clouds to weather stations in different locations on the ground.

weathering (weth′ər iŋ) The physical and chemical processes by which rock is broken down into smaller pieces. (A10) Cracks in rock produced by freezing rainwater or the growth of plant roots are examples of *weathering*.

wind (wind) The movement of air over Earth's surface. (E21) The strong *wind* lifted the kite high above the houses.

windsock (wind′säk) A device used to show wind direction, consisting of a cloth bag that is open at both ends and hung on a pole. (E38) The *windsock* showed that the wind was blowing from the north.

wind vane (wind vān) A device, often shaped like an arrow, used to show the direction of the wind. (E38) The *wind vane* on the roof of the weather station showed that the wind was blowing from the southwest.

INDEX

*Activity
Bold heads indicate Teaching Guide material.

*Activity
Bold heads indicate Teaching Guide material.